BRAIDING

Marva Patterson

BRAIDING

Marva Patterson

Milady Publishing Company
(A Division of Delmar Publishers Inc.)
Two Computer Drive, West
Albany, New York 12212

Editor: Catherine Frangie

Production Manager: John Mickelbank

Art Coordinator: John Fornieri

Artist: Mshindo Kuumba I.

Cover Design: Our Designs, Inc.

Copyright © 1992
Milady Publishing Company
(A Division of Delmar Publishers Inc.)

ISBN 0-87350-3864

Printed in the United States of America

10 9 8 7 6 5 4 3 2 1

ACKNOWLEDGMENTS

I am deeply grateful to Rabie Patterson Harris, my sister, for contributing Chapters 1 and 2 (History of Braids and Why Braids Were Worn in the Past).

For her poem "Beauty and Hair Braids," I would like to thank Matilda Efua Aborowi Garbrah-Davis of Ghana.

I am also pleased to express my thanks to Cathy Frangie, Cosmetology Editor at Milady Publishing Company, for imparting ideas and suggestions for the overall outcome of the text; Mr. Steve Hoffman, Vice President of Marketing for Milady Publishing Company, for his suggestions, for keeping the text organized and unified; and to all staff members of Milady Publishing Company who contributed in the design, production and marketing of this text.

Finally, I give thanks to all my models for their patience and dependability; special thanks to Penny Carter for always being there when I needed her, Carla Radford for assisting with scheduling for the models, Damaris Lugo for assisting with make-up, Tina Moore, Michele Mannette, Arlene and Radine Jennings. I wish to acknowledge the assistance of Leothy Owens and Sonia Benton in getting models to their appointments. Thanks also to Evelyn Kormanik, my typist, who also assisted me in getting the models together; Ken Jones, make-up artist; Caroline Ross for make-up and photography; Kwame Braithwaite, photographer; Mshindo, artist; Tony Lasala, photographer; Bridgitte Holder, Mary Healey, Robin Jackson, Bernice Calvin, Jon Carlton, Marion Alexander, Arnetha Curry, Gayle DeWees, Florin and Salome Ionascu, William Scudder, Yolanda Lester, and Armando Blackman (my old classmates from Wilfred Beauty Academy) for their faith in me and the project; all members of my family, especially Yvonne Darden and Vilma Osborne, two of my sisters, for their inspiration; Augustine Ryan, my youngest daughter's godmother, for all her encouragement, and for assisting with selecting braid extension styles for Chapters 4 and 7.

ABOUT THE AUTHOR

Master braider Marva Patterson has been creating braids and hair extensions on a daily basis for over 13 years. A former fashion designer and furrier, Ms. Patterson is a licensed cosmetologist who holds a degree in chemistry and is certified by the American Chemical Society.

CONTENTS

CHAPTER 5

How to Prepare Client's Hair Before Braiding is Done

CHAPTER 6

How to do Braid Extensions

CHAPTER 7

A Pictorial of Braid Extension Styles

CHAPTER 8

How to Eliminate Fuzziness of Short Hair Coming Through in Cornrow Type Extensions

CHAPTER 9

How to Care for and Maintain Braid Extensions

CHAPTER 10

How to Introduce and Promote Braid Extensions in Your Beauty Salon

BEAUTY IN HAIR BRAIDS

Mother Nature has endowed us
With the beauty of hair.
The shapes and sizes of different heads
Indifferent of length, thickness and texture
Can be given a most attractive style with braids.

The African woman with braided hair
Receives a romantic gaze from her suitors.
She displays her carefully parted lines
And interwoven designs of hair extensions
Portrayed to show the artistic flair with braids.

Peoples of all races, irrespective of color,
Are beautified by the skillful hands of
One who patiently gives a new look to one's hair.
The natural instinct to look self-confident,
The radiance and glow adds to make the result
A flattering and appreciative one.

Original poem by
Matilda Efua Aborowi Garbrah-Davis
of Ghana

December 24, 1989

PREFACE

"Braiding" explains and illustrates how hair braid extensions can be undetectably applied in both visible and invisible braids, for males and females with different textures of hair — straight, curly and tightly curled.

The text also explains how braid extensions can be used for beauty and to remedy chemically-abused hair. The different types of additional hair used for braid extensions, their availability, cost, ability to be processed with or without chemicals, their durability after processing, and their ability to have color added or removed are also discussed.

The chief goals of this text are to help beauty school instructors, cosmetology students and cosmetologists select the right braid techniques to be used for clients with chemically-damaged hair, select the right type of additional hair to achieve a particular style, ensure clients' comfort during the lengthy braid extension process, practice applying undetectable braid extensions, practice acquiring good finger dexterity, and help clients with proper care and maintenance of braid extensions.

"Braiding" can also be helpful to braiders, braid clients and potential braid clients. The braider can better understand applying braid extensions and see how different types of additional hair affect the outcome of a braid style. The braid client and potential braid clients can view before-and-after pictures of models to see how braid extensions can enhance or change their present hair style.

CHAPTER

1 INTRODUCTION

From ancient times, men and women have engaged in the art of fashioning their hair. Wendy Cooper, author of *Hair, Sex, Society, Symbolism,* describes man's drive to change and improve his appearance and status.

"Once the human race discovered that hair was good tempered, pliable and regenerative, and could be cut, shaved, shaped, dyed, braided, crimped, curled, waved, puffed, padded, and frizzed, it proceeded to use hair in a variety of permutations of length, style and color, in the long, continuous search for novelty, beauty, and status, sometimes called fashion."

Documentation of early hairstyles is scarce, but evidence from tombs of Egyptians, Assyrians, Sumerians, Chaldeans and other groups from 3200 B.C. to 400 A.D. provides information about prevailing hairstyles. The early Egyptians—perhaps for religious purposes, to indicate rank or keep a healthy, clean scalp in the hot Egyptian climate—shaved their heads, adorning them with elaborate ornaments. Others covered their shaved heads with wigs and braids. Braids of all sizes, set in beeswax or other stiffening agents, were used in many different ways.

As an integral part of their culture, some West African tribes used braids in their hair styles. Hundreds of styles can be traced to countries, tribes and regions in Africa. The art of braiding was usually passed on from one female member of a family to another—from mother to daughter, from aunt to niece. The process of braiding the hair into a work of art could take less than an hour, or hours, depending on the style desired. In Nigeria, Fulani women interwove false pieces of hair with their own hair to create beautiful long braid hairstyles. These false pieces were generally passed down from one generation to another. In certain East African tribes, men wore elaborate hairstyles of matted hair intertwined with beads, ostrich and parrot feathers, shells, pieces of ivory. Women wore braids, usually bound with thread to make varied coil designs that could be twisted or woven into many styles. Or they wore braids without threads. Fiber or sticks were sometimes needed to create a bridge or the cap-shaped hairstyles. Hairstyles could be named for the number of braids used in a particular style, or for a special occasion or event. Europeans, Asians and Indians from North and South America have worn braids, with or without adornments, for many years.

Americans have been braiding their hair for centuries. Braids were worn mainly by younger girls, and were rarely worn in public. But in the 1960's, a time of unrest and the awakening of a black cultural identity, braid styles became a way for black Americans to identify with their roots and express their individuality. Braid styles took the form of cornrows or individual braids, with extensions considered to be the more modern style. These two braid forms were braided simply or intricately and worn with or without ornaments of beads, shells, bells, rings and charms. The reaction to wearing braids as a hairstyle has not always been positive or accepting in America. The case of Pamela Mitchel, who was asked by her employer to change her braid style, exemplifies the negative attitude toward braids. Ms. Mitchel had to file a law suit against her employer to continue wearing her hair as she wished.

The eighties saw a new surge in the popularity of braid styles. Males and females of all age groups and cultural backgrounds are wearing braids with a feeling of freedom. Most hair salons offer braiding services, and braiders are still sought out for their skills in creating beautiful braid styles. Braiding as a domestic art form has been around for centuries and will continue in the future. The popularity of braid styles may grow or ebb as all fashions do, but the imprint the art form of braiding has made on the lives of many will be felt for a long time.

CHAPTER

2 WHY BRAIDS WERE WORN IN THE PAST

People wearing braids come from all different cultural, social, economic, age and sex groups, and their reasons for wearing braids are as varied as the styles.

Thousands of years ago the Egyptians shaved their heads and wore wigs and braids because they believed shaving strengthened the skull. Phoenician women also shaved their heads and wore wigs so they could sacrifice their hair to the gods. In Nigeria, Yoruba men and women wore special braid hairdos in homage to their gods and goddesses. One braided hairstyle might be dedicated to the god of thunder, another to the river goddess.

It was even possible to name someone's tribe or town of origin simply by the braid style they wore. Like name plates, braid styles marked one's social and marital status, age, religious and political affiliation. They also symbolized important community events like the birth of a first child. Special styles were used in coming-of-age ceremonies—such as the Ejiji and Ipako—in which nine thin braids were plaited horizontally across the head. Braid styles were used symbolically to signify the fertility status of a woman; one style announced the birth of a first child; another pointed to a childless wife and still others meant a pregnancy. Some hairstyles sent the message—"spinster," "married woman," "mourning woman," "barren woman." Hairstyles were also used to attract the sexes to each other, to depict an object or commemorate a significant event.

In her article, "Wearing Coils: Nigerian Hair Sculpture," Norma Rosen tells the story of how building the EKO Bridge in Lagos, capital of Nigeria, became the catalyst for creating a braid style that reflected the structure. Similarly, the braid style, "Police Cap," was introduced to commemorate the first entry of women into the Nigerian police force.

Hairdressers are strongly influenced by the social, economic and political climates of their times. They are keenly sensitive to hairstyles that are "in," that are appropriate, that are significant to a particular time—and will blend their knowledge of their times with the desires of their clients to arrange the most flattering braid styles.

Today, hairstylists are noting changing attitudes toward braid styles. More traditional styles are still worn, but the social, political and personal reasons behind wearing a particular style have changed. In the eighties and nineties, braid styles are worn for beauty and to remedy damaged hair. People are wearing styles they find fashionable and attractive. It is the individual's prerogative to choose his or her own style. Today, you may create a combination of different styles for your clients—with a side view depicting one style, the back view another, and the front yet another.

For many Americans, wearing braids has taken on a new meaning. Braids are associated with racial identity, glamour, success, spiritual strength and physical vitality. Men and women have adapted styles to suit their unique needs. Braiding as fashion has crossed cultural, social and economic lines, and many people with many different textures of hair wear braids.

Braid extensions let your clients with chemically abused hair look their best while waiting for new hair growth; these clients do not have to cut off all their damaged hair or worry about further breakage. Braid extensions are ideal for clients with tightly curled hair that has been chemically relaxed, and must be periodically touched up with the chemical. If the hair is not touched up, combing from tightly curled hair to straight ends creates a pull on hair.. Constant pulling on the hair will eventually cause an excessive amount of breakage. Braid extensions totally eliminate this breakage problem.

While wearing braid extensions, your clients can rest their hair totally from relaxers, pulling, excessive combing and brushing, and trying to force their hair into styles they know are impossible to achieve. This resting period allows hair to grow in without interference. In fact, when hair is left to grow in freely— along with proper diet, enough rest, and proper maintenance of braid extensions and scalp (to be discussed further in Chapter 9)—it can grow in much longer and thicker.

Braid extensions can be used on young women, mature women and children, while some men find wearing braid extensions quite sexy.

For young people on the go, braid extensions are ideal since they allow them to spend little or no time on their hair. For the businesswoman who doesn't want an obvious braid look, there's the option of invisible braiding.

Braid extensions for the mature woman can be braided in any style if you wisely select the right length and amount of hair. The mature woman can also enjoy the most intricate upstyles, and if desired, a touch of gray. Braid extensions for children should be kept simple. A child wearing braid extensions can be a real joy for a working mother, since additional hair added to a child's hair makes braid work last longer and look neater without daily combing.

Braid extensions, for beauty alone or as a remedy for chemically abused hair, allow women, children and men to wake up looking terrific and keep looking great all during a busy day.

CHAPTER

3 WHY BRAIDS ARE BEING WORN TODAY

Today, hair braiding is worn for its beauty and to remedy hair damaged by strong chemicals.

Hair braiding in the 90's has become a craze, particularly among black women, since it isn't just braiding hair, but the art of adding additional hair to achieve immediate length and body without fear of detection. The process of adding additional hair is called braid extensions. Visible or not, braid extensions can help create the most intricate style, no matter how short or sparse the hair might be.

Chemically abused hair is usually caused by improper use of chemicals containing caustic reagents such as sodium hydroxide, calcium hydroxide or ammonium thioglycolate. The three reagents above are listed in order of decreasing causticity. It is important for you to know the degree of damage these chemicals can cause if used improperly, since the degree of hair damage determines the braid extension technique (to be discussed in this chapter). If you forget the decreasing order of causticity of the three reagents discussed, you need only rely on the pH factor for any chemical in question. Note: the higher the pH, the quicker the chemical reaction and the greater the degree of hair damage (keeping in mind that pH balance is 7.0).

Sodium hydroxide or lye, the strongest of the three reagents listed, can do the most damage to hair when used improperly. When sodium hydroxide is used to relax hair, usually tightly curled hair, it leaves hair very straight and somewhat limp. If used incorrectly—by overprocessing, excessive overlapping or incomplete neutralizing—sodium hydroxide can dissolve or eat away hair shafts.

Calcium hydroxide is not as strong as sodium hydroxide, and most manufacturers refer to it as "No Lye." When used to relax hair, calcium hydroxide leaves it straight, robbing it of body. It does not leave hair as limp as sodium hydroxide would.

If calcium hydroxide is used improperly by overprocessing, excessive overlapping or incomplete neutralizing, it can eat away the hair shaft, but to a lesser degree than sodium hydroxide.

Ammonium thioglycolate, a waving agent, can be used with rods on straight hair to create an "S-formation" that turns straight hair curly. It can also be used as a pre-straightener for tightly curled hair. Hair is then wrapped on rods to produce the

"S-formation"—turning the tightly curled hair straight and then curly. Ammonium thioglycolate is the weakest of the three reagents discussed, but unfortunately, if used improperly—by overprocessing, oversaturating the scalp with chemicals, rolling rods too tightly or incomplete neutralizing—ammonium thioglycolate can take hair out from the roots, making it look thin.

When doing braid extensions on hair damaged by improper use of sodium or calcium hydroxide, you can add a small (roughly 10-40 strands) or average amount (roughly 100 strands or more) of additional hair to hair that has been properly prepared for braid work—without concern that the weight of the added hair will pull out the client's own hair. Hair damaged by improper use of ammonium thioglycolate can accept small amounts of additional hair since the hair is usually quite thin due to loss from the roots.

Braid extensions let your clients with chemically abused hair look their best while waiting for new hair growth; these clients do not have to cut off all their damaged hair or worry about further breakage. Braid extensions are ideal for clients with tightly curled hair that has been chemically relaxed, and must be periodically touched up with the chemical. If the hair is not touched up, combing from tightly curled hair to straight ends creates a pull on hair. Constant pulling on the hair will eventually cause an excessive amount of breakage. Braid extensions totally eliminate this breakage problem.

While wearing braid extensions, your clients can rest their hair totally from relaxers, pulling, excessive combing and brushing, and trying to force their hair into styles they know are impossible to achieve. This resting period allows hair to grow in without interference. In fact, when hair is left to grow in freely—along with proper diet, enough rest, and proper maintenance of braid extensions and scalp (to be discussed further in Chapter 9)—it can grow in much longer and thicker.

Braid extensions can be used on young women, mature women and children, while some men find wearing braid extensions quite sexy.

For young people on the go, braid extensions are ideal since they allow them to spend little or no time on their hair. For the businesswoman who doesn't want an obvious braid look, there's the option of invisible braiding.

Braid extensions for the mature woman can be braided in any style if you wisely select the right length and amount of hair. The mature woman can also enjoy the most intricate up-styles, and if desired, a touch of gray. Braid extensions for children should be kept simple. A child wearing braid extensions can be a real joy for a working mother, since additional hair added to a child's hair makes braid work last longer and look neater without daily combing.

Braid extensions, for beauty alone or as a remedy for chemically abused hair, allow women, children and men to wake up looking terrific and keep looking great all during a busy day.

CHAPTER
4 DIFFERENT TYPES OF HAIR USED TO CREATE PARTICULAR STYLES

In this chapter we will discuss the different types of hair used for braiding extensions. We will also talk about their expense, availability for purchase, ability to be processed with or without chemicals, reactions to chemicals, durability after processing, and capacity to have color added or removed.

It is vitally important for conscientious students and cosmetologists concerned about creating a specific braid style to know about the different types of hair used in braiding. You should also be familiar with their physical properties and potential to be chemically changed. This information is vital, since different styles depend on the type of hair used.

Although synthetic and oriental hair are the most common types of hair used for braiding extensions, Yak hair, European hair and Indian hair can also be used.

Synthetic Hair

Of the different types of hair mentioned, synthetic hair is the least expensive. Synthetic hair is light weight and tangles easily when being used. It can be readily purchased from beauty and hair supply stores, wig shops, discount stores and some drugstores. Since synthetic hair is man-made and lacks the cell structure of human hair, it does not respond to chemical processes. However, it can take on a wavy, crimped or spiral curl look when processed non-chemically by manufacturers. When buying synthetic hair, it is important to choose the exact color desired, since color cannot be added or removed chemically. Color can be physically sprayed or painted on desired areas, but the effect is only temporary. If shampooed in very warm water, combed or brushed and air-dried, synthetic hair will lose its wavy, crimped or spiral curl formation. However, the wavy, crimped or curled formation can be retained if synthetic hair is shampooed gently using tepid water, rinsed in cool water, then shaped into the desired style with your finger instead of a comb or brush before air drying. Synthetic hair looks great in up-styles, and it is not easy to detect that synthetic instead of human hair is being used. Therefore, when you're doing up-

4.1a Before.

4.1b After (with synthetic hair used for this invisible braid extension style).

styles, it's more economical to use synthetic hair for braiding than human hair.

Unfortunately, synthetic hair does not look attractive for the total braided-down look without beads or closers, since the only way to keep the ends of the hair closed is to wrap the ends or burn them together. These closing procedures leave an unpleasant appearance. For the wavy, crimped and curly braid styles—all usually partially braided with the ends left loose—synthetic hair processed by manufacturers can be used to create beautiful, inexpensive styles. (See figs. 4.1a and 4.1b.)

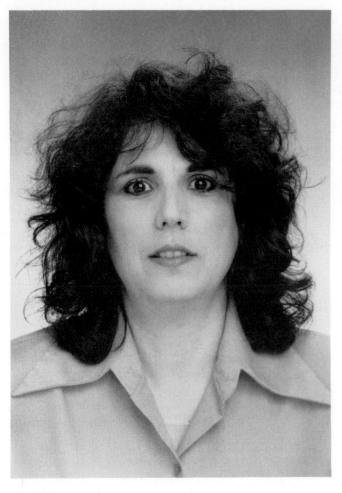

4.2a Before.

4.2b After (with Oriental hair used for this visible braid extension style).

Oriental Hair

Although Oriental hair is much more expensive than synthetic, it is the most commonly used hair for braiding extensions. Oriental hair is relatively soft, but not as soft as Indian or European hair. In partially braided styles with loose ends, Oriental hair can get quite puffy, which works well for styles that need such body. (See figs. 4.2a and 4.2b.) You can buy Oriental hair from hair suppliers, beauty supply stores and some wig shops. It is very strong and can be successfully processed with strong chemicals to go from straight to wavy, curly or tightly curled hair with little worry of destroying the hair. This chemical processing is permanent, so there should be no concern about the process being removed when shampooing, combing or brushing. Oriental hair comes in a variety of colors. If you buy a lighter color by mistake, or if the hair turns lighter from too much sun, it can be easily darkened by tinting or rinsing. However, it is difficult to tint Oriental hair to lighter shades. Bleaching the hair for a long time to get lighter shades can be done, but removing color is troublesome and the bleaching process is not worth the time or effort. If your clients using Oriental hair want a lighter streak or streaks, it is better to purchase the desired amount of a lighter color to be braided in as a streak or streaks. Oriental hair looks terrific regardless of the braid extension style your clients might choose. It can be braided in up-styles; invisible braid extension styles done in straight, wavy, curly or tightly curled hair; or braid extension styles braided all the way to the ends, since the hair will stay relatively closed without unattractive wrapping or burning. If a temporary curly style is desired, Oriental hair can be successfully thermal roller curled or thermal croquignoled curled without excessive heat from the curler harming the hair.

Yak Hair

Yak hair is a very coarse, straight hair that comes from a long-haired bovine mammal usually found in the mountains of central Asia. Since Yak hair comes from a warm-blooded animal, it is usually sold as human hair. It is a little more expensive than Oriental hair. Yak hair is not as available as Oriental hair and can only be purchased from some hair suppliers.

Due to the extreme coarseness of Yak hair, it is very difficult to chemically change its structure from straight to wavy or curly,

4.3a Before.

4.3b After (with Yak hair used for this invisible braid extension style). See a "Special Note," in Chapter 6, for braid extension technique used.

and this process is usually unsuccessful. Yak hair can be tinted or rinsed to darker shades. Like Oriental hair, it is very hard to lighten, and it is not worth the time or effort. If your clients want a lighter streak or streaks with Yak hair, it is better to buy a lighter color already processed by the manufacturer. Yak hair looks terrific if coarse, straight, invisible braid styles are preferred. Straight, invisible braid styles with Yak hair differ from the same styles done with Oriental hair because Oriental hair tends to look puffy, while Yak hair styles stay straight down without puffiness. (See figs. 4.3a and 4.3b.) Yak hair partially braided with ends left opened gives beautiful coarse, straight, invisible braid styles.

If your clients want a total braided-down style that looks coarse and stays straight down, it is best to mix Yak hair with Oriental hair to keep the braided ends relatively closed. A mixture of 30% Oriental and 70% Yak hair is a good combination to achieve such styles. If a temporary curl is desired, Yak hair can be thermal roller curled or thermal croquignoled curled without worry of heat damage.

Indian Hair

Indian hair is more expensive than Yak hair. It is soft and straight, but not as soft as European hair. (See figs. 4.4a and 4.4b.) Indian hair is not often used for braid extensions, but if your clients cannot afford the more expensive European hair, they

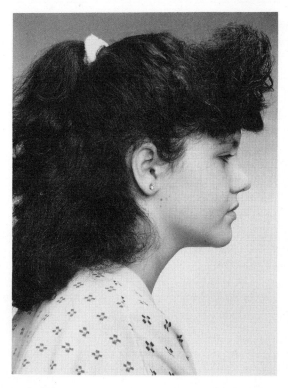

4.4a Before.

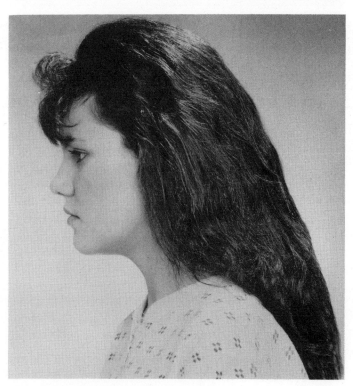

4.4b After (with Indian hair used for this invisible braid extension style). See a "Special Note," in Chapter 6, for braid extension technique used.

can use Indian hair for a similar look. Indian hair is not very available and can only be bought from some hair suppliers. It can be processed with mild chemicals to go from straight to wavy or curly without damaging the hair. Chemically processing Indian hair to produce a wavy or curly formation is permanent, so you don't have to worry about removing the process when shampooing, combing or brushing. Indian hair can be purchased in different colors, or it can be tinted to look darker. However, it is very difficult to tint or rinse Indian hair to lighter shades. If a lighter streak or streaks are desired, it is better to buy a lighter color processed by the manufacturer than to try to make Indian hair lighter.

Although Indian hair is not as soft as European hair, it can be used to braid lovely invisible braid extension styles similar to those using European hair. With Indian hair, styles that are to be braided down to the ends can have a soft, straight look without puffiness. Braided ends can also remain relatively closed. If there is a problem with closing braided ends, 20-30% of Oriental hair can be mixed with the Indian hair to assure better closing of ends without losing the soft straight-down look. If a temporary curl style is desired, Indian hair can be successfully thermal roller curled or thermal croquignoled curled without hair being damaged by heat from the curlers.

European Hair

European hair is the most expensive and softest of the five basic hair types used for braid extensions. (See figs. 4.5a and 4.5b.) However, it is not commonly used for braid extensions and is not very easy to buy, though some hair suppliers do sell it. European hair can be successfully processed with mild chemicals to go from straight to wavy or curly without destroying the hair. When European hair is chemically treated to make a wavy or curly formation, the process is considered permanent and the formation will not be removed when shampooed, combed or brushed. European hair can be purchased in different colors, and if you wish to change European hair to a darker shade, the color can be achieved by tinting or rinsing. However, if your clients want a lighter shade of streak or streaks, it's better to purchase a lighter color processed by the manufacturers.

When partially braided with ends loose, European hair gives the softest-looking straight, wavy and curly invisible braid extension styles of all the five types of hair. Since European hair is very expensive, you should not use it in up-styles, but partially braided-down where the soft ends can be left out to be enjoyed. If braided all the way to the ends, however, European hair can remain relatively closed since its ends are soft and will

4.5a Before.

4.5b After (with European hair used for this invisible braid extension style).

not puff. For a temporary curl style, European hair can be thermal roller curled or thermal croquignoled curled without being destroyed by heat from the curlers.

Summary

Of the five types of hair used for braiding extensions—synthetic, Oriental, Yak, Indian and European—synthetic is the least expensive; Oriental is moderately priced, but because of its manageability may be less expensive than synthetic hair in the long run; and European is the most expensive. If clients cannot afford European hair, synthetic hair already processed by manufacturers can be used to obtain beautiful, inexpensive wavy, curled or crimped styles. Clients who can afford to purchase European hair should, since they will certainly get the softest-looking straight, wavy and curly invisible braid extension styles.

Due to its ability to be chemically processed, Oriental hair can withstand stronger chemicals than either Indian or European. When chemically processed, Oriental hair can go from straight to wavy, to curly and tightly curled and can be reused over and over without losing its wave or curl formation because of its manageability. In contrast, it is quite difficult to chemically process Yak hair to change its structure to wavy or curly. Synthetic hair, on the other hand, can only be processed to be wavy or curly temporarily by manufacturers. If preprocessed formations become undone, synthetic hair can be set or repurchased.

Overall, you can see how familiarity with the five different hair types used in braid extensions allows you to select and purchase the proper type of hair to achieve a specific style.

CHAPTER

5 HOW TO PREPARE CLIENTS' HAIR BEFORE BRAIDING IS DONE

Before doing braid extensions, you should consult with your client to determine whether their hair is damaged. Also consider the shape of your client's face and head to help them select a flattering braid style.

Your client's lifestyle and profession are also major factors in choosing the best style. Deciding on the type of hair to be used to achieve the most becoming style is the most important aspect of your consultation. It is also important to check to see if your client's hair has been chemically damaged, and to what degree. Clients should be questioned as to what type of chemical had been used on their hair. If they do not recall what chemical had been used, you can refer back to Chapter Three to get a general idea of what kind of chemical might have been used, based on the damage. After deciding what kind of chemical damage the client might have, proceed by referring to Chapter Three for the braiding techniques that apply.

If there is any injury to the scalp, such as opened lesions, you should recommend that the client be first treated by a dermatologist before braiding. If your client has a problem with pityriasis (dandruff), treat the scalp by using oil as a cleansing treatment and then shampooing to leave hair oil-free and rid of dandruff. If your client's scalp is clear from open lesions or dandruff, wash hair with a mild shampoo and then condition. Make sure to apply conditioner to scalp and over hair shaft, paying extra attention to the ends of hair which tend to be damaged. Rinse and blow-dry hair after spraying with a vitamin or protein infusium product that conditions the hair and protects it from the excessive heat of the blow dryer.

After this treatment, your client's hair will be clean, well conditioned, totally oil-free and ready to be braided. If your clients are planning to shampoo and prepare their hair before braid extensions, advise them in advance that their hair should be clean, well conditioned and oil-free before coming in for service. Having the client's hair oil-free for braiding extension work is vitally important, since it lets you get a good grasp on your client's hair, especially if it's very short.

Basic Implements Used for Braiding Extensions

Having all the implements prepared and at hand before doing braid extensions is very important. Proper preparation saves time and, most of all, helps you work more efficiently and be in full control of the situation during the braiding process.

The basic implements used for braid extensions are: 1) A tail comb—with a pointed metal end to be used when doing braid extensions to achieve precise parting of your client's hair. 2) Butterfly clips—used to keep the portion of your client's hair not ready to be braided out of the way. 3) A rubber blow drying brush—to brush the loose ends of partially braided extensions or invisible braid extension styles before cutting. 4) A large comb—to be used to comb out your client's hair so it can be sectioned, preferably on clients with straight hair. 5) A detangler comb—for clients with curly hair, to comb out hair by sectioning. 6) A pick—to be used to pick out and free the client's hair for sectioning, preferably on customers with tightly curled hair. 7) Sharp scissors—for cutting and shaping braid styles into their desired form. 8) Thinning shears—to remove any undesired bulk

5.1 Basic implements and equipment used for braiding extensions.

A. Tail comb with pointed metal end
B. Rubber blow drying brush
C. Butterfly clip
D. Plastic pick
E. Detangler comb
F. Clipper
G. Razor
H. Sharp scissors
I. Hair extension

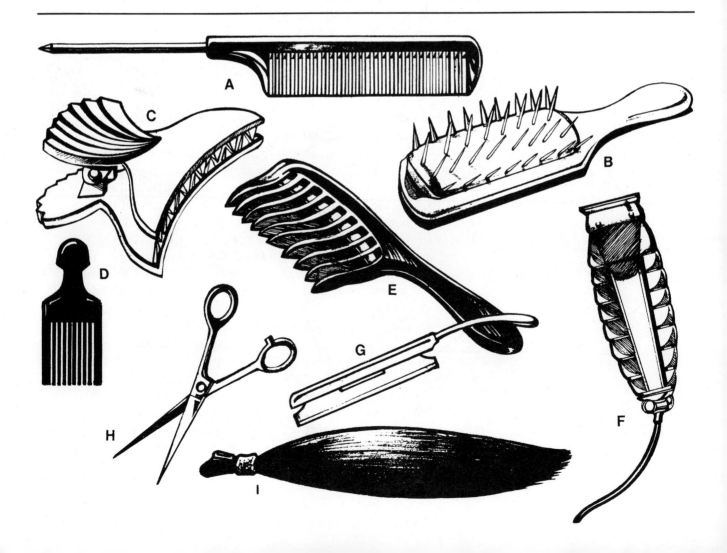

from braiding extension styles. 9) A razor—to be used to create a feathery end on braid extension styles, preferably on straighter hair. 10) Clippers—to be used to remove unruly hair at the nape of your client's neck, preferably on braid extension styles done into up-styles. 11) A cape or gown—to protect your client's clothing. 12) A pillow—to be placed on the back of the chair under the client's head. The pillow is generally used when doing cornrows and braids directed toward the back of the client's head to alleviate the pressure exerted on the neck. 13) An hydraulic chair—used to raise and lower your client's sitting position as needed. 14) A spray water bottle—used to wet your client's hair if the style requires wetting after braiding has been completed. 15) Hair to be used for braid extensions—hair should be a minimum of 1/2 pound in weight for a full head of braid extension work. However, less hair can be used for children's styles. 16) A high stool with back—used by students and cosmetologists—in which you can be seated comfortably with your back firmly supported during the long hours needed to do braid extensions.

These implements can be categorized and separated into three groups. (See fig. 5.1)

J. High stool
K. Pillow
L. Hydraulic chair
M. Cape
N. Adjustable chair
O. Spray bottle
P. Thinning shears
Q. Large comb

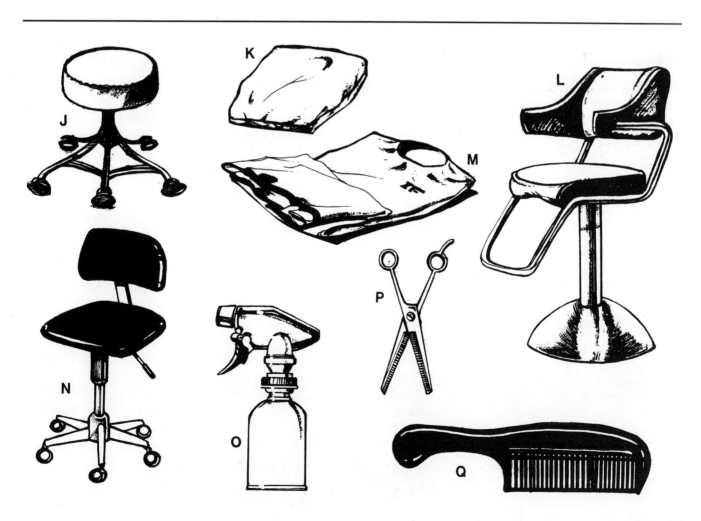

Implements for:

Straight Hair	Curly Hair	Tightly Curled Hair
Tail comb with a pointed metal end	Tail comb with a pointed metal end	Tail comb with a pointed metal end
Several butterfly clips	Several butterfly clips	Several butterfly clips
Rubber blow drying brush	Rubber blow drying brush	Rubber blow drying brush
Sharp scissors	Sharp scissors	Sharp scissors
Thinning shears	Thinning shears	Thinning shears
Razor	Razor	Razor
Clipper	Clipper	Clipper
Cape or gown	Cape or gown	Cape or gown
Large comb	Detangler comb	Plastic pick
Pillow	Pillow	Pillow
Hydraulic chair	Hydraulic chair	Hydraulic chair
Spray bottle	Spray bottle	Spray bottle
1/2 lb. or more hair	1/2 lb. or more hair	1/2 lb. or more hair
High stool	High stool	High stool

How Additional Hair Used for Braid Extensions Should be Handled to Avoid Waste

It is important to know how to properly handle the different types of hair used for braid extensions to prevent the hair from tangling and becoming too disorderly to work with. This also avoids wasting great amounts of hair.

When you buy Oriental, Yak, Indian or European hair, they are usually sold by weight and tied with a cord. However, Oriental hair from a wig shop or discount store is usually prepackaged in quarter pound sizes and cannot be bought by the ounce as needed. For example, if nine ounces of hair are needed, you would have to buy three packages, equaling twelve ounces. Synthetic hair, very light weight and easy to tangle, is always prepackaged and sold by a standard amount, not by weight.

When using Oriental, Yak, Indian or European hair purchased from hair suppliers, the cord can be removed before braiding, and the hair then placed on a flat surface. If you are right handed, place your left hand, with the palm facing down, on the bundle of hair, pushing it against the flat surface while using your right hand to grasp about 1/20th of the bundle, pulling off hair abruptly. (See fig. 5.2a.) This instantly allows a uniform amount of hair to be pulled off and prevents hair from wasteful tangling. Place the rest of the bundle off to the side within reach.

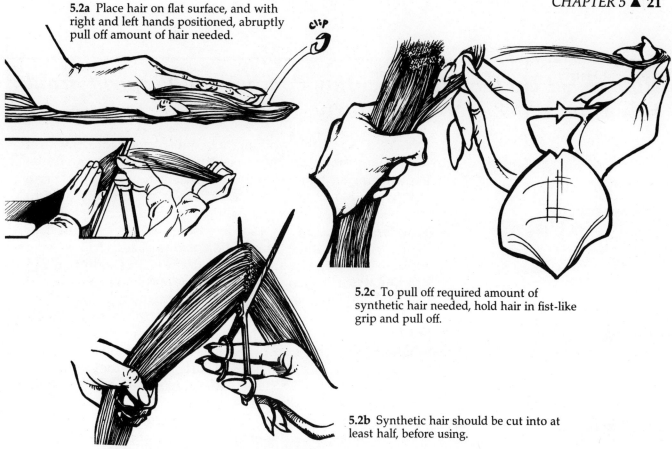

5.2a Place hair on flat surface, and with right and left hands positioned, abruptly pull off amount of hair needed.

5.2c To pull off required amount of synthetic hair needed, hold hair in fist-like grip and pull off.

5.2b Synthetic hair should be cut into at least half, before using.

Then proceed with the braiding, using, in desired portions as needed, the 1/20th amount of hair that has been removed. When the 1/20th portion of hair has been used up, an additional 1/20th section should be pulled off and used as discussed until all required amounts of hair for the particular style have been used up. Note that Oriental hair, which might be sold cord-tied by hair suppliers or packaged by wig shops or discount stores, should be opened and handled as discussed.

Synthetic hair should be handled differently. Usually sold in packages, synthetic hair is very long, about four feet (48 inches) or more. It is then folded in half before being packaged. Before braiding with synthetic hair, cut the hair into at least half, or an appropriate length based on the type of style selected. (See fig. 5.2b.) After synthetic hair has been cut accordingly, hold the synthetic hair, in a fist-like grip, straight up. If you are right handed, hold the bulk of the hair with your left hand, gradually feeding bits of the hair with the fingers of your left hand to the fingers of your right hand. Your right hand then holds the hair that was fed to it very securely, pulling a small amount of hair out to the right about 1/20th while making sure to pull hair all the way to the ends. (See fig. 5.2c.) The rest of the hair should be put aside within reach. Then you can use the 1/20th portion that was pulled off for braiding. After the 1/20th portion has been used up, repeat the procedure.

How to Set Up the Proper Seating Positions to Perform Braid Extension Work More Effectively

Proper set-up of the working area and correct adjustment of seating positions are just as important as having all the implements on hand to perform braid extension work more effectively. Make sure your work area is set up according to whether you are left or right handed. Your implements should be well-organized and in reach to ensure a continuous, effective braiding session. If the back portion of your client's hair is being braided, adjust the hydraulic chair to the right height to avoid bending while braiding. When the front portion of your client's hair is being braided, the chair should be lowered. When cornrows or braids are directed toward the back of your client's head, the chair should be pumped up to its maximum, and a pillow placed on the back of the chair under your client's head to alleviate neck strain. (See fig. 5.3.) Place a small stool or chair in front of client as a foot rest. Note that your client's body position is now slanted as illustrated.

A final note: fingernails should be at moderate length, and make sure there are no split or broken nails that will pull your clients' hair.

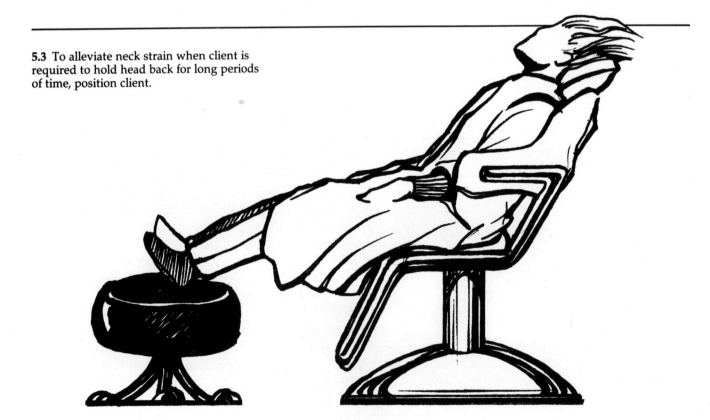

5.3 To alleviate neck strain when client is required to hold head back for long periods of time, position client.

CHAPTER

6 HOW TO DO BRAID EXTENSIONS

This chapter will explain how to do braid extensions and apply them undetectably. Step-by-step illustrations are given on applying undetectable braid extensions—visible and invisible, individual and cornrow, and individual and cornrow extensions combined. The art of feeding in extra additional hair to have a proportioned larger braid is explained and illustrated. Also discussed is the importance of the direction in which extensions are applied to give length, body and exaggerated height to hair. Good finger dexterity, precise partings and control over braid extension are also stressed and illustrated.

Concluding this chapter are illustrations and explanations on how to do two simple and one intricate braid extension style. Now that you have learned how to do precise partings, the art of feeding in extra additional hair, good finger technique, etc., you can combine all these skills to create not only the intricate designs shown but an endless variety of styles.

How to Make Partings for Individual Braid Extensions

Partings for individual braid extensions are in a brick-like formation as shown. (See fig. 6.1a.)

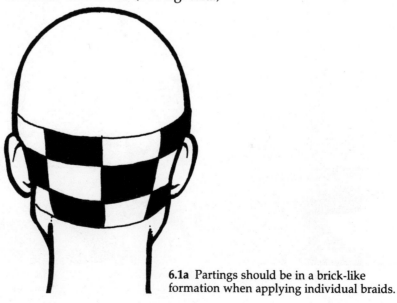

6.1a Partings should be in a brick-like formation when applying individual braids.

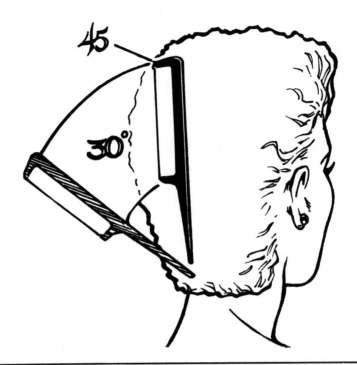

6.1b Hold tail comb at 45° angle, then gradually slant comb 30° to left.

If braid extensions are to begin at the nape of client's neck, the first part can start about 1/8″ to 5/8″ above the nape.

▲ Hold tail comb with its metal ending pointing downward at 45° angle from client's scalp where part is desired.

▲ Comb will gradually slant in the opposite direction of part at about a 30° angle from scalp as shown. (See fig. 6.1b.)

NOTE:

As part is being made—starting at left going to right—metal end of tail comb should not be raised away from client's scalp; there should be one continuous straight part without lifting comb. (See fig. 6.1c.)

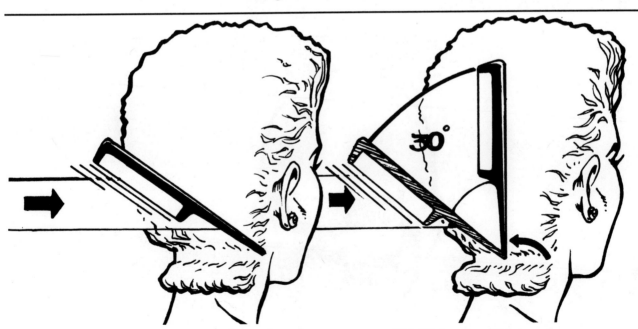

6.1c One continuous straight part is made from left to right without lifting comb 1/8″— 5/8″ above nape.

6.1d If it is not possible to make one continuous part, place tail comb 1/2″ before the end of present part at 45° — using as a guideline to complete part at 30°.

6.1e Make vertical part 1/8″—5/8″ to acquire the partings for an individual braid.

6.1f Braid individual braid.

If it is not possible to make one continuous part across, use the part that is already made as a guideline. The instructions already given on how to begin the part should be followed by placing metal end of tail comb 1/2″ before the end of present part at a 45° angle; then slant 30° according to previous instruction and continue parting across as shown. (See fig. 6.1d.)

▲ 1/8″-5/8″ part has been made horizontally above the nape of client's neck from left to right, then a 1/8″-5/8″ vertical part can be made, giving the parts required for an individual braid extension. (See fig. 6.1e.)

▲ Braid the individual braid. (See fig. 6.1f.)

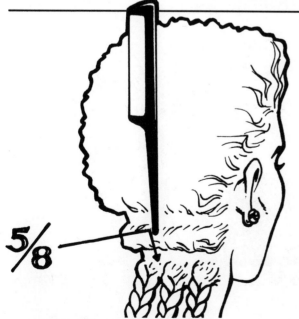

6.1g Part 2nd row 1/8″—5/8″ above previous row then 1/8″—5/8″ down vertically to acquire partings for individual braid as in fig. 6.1d.

6.1h Brick-like formation partings will conceal all partings of previous row.

▲ After braiding individual braids across the 1st row, part 2nd row 1/8″—5/8″ above previous row, then 1/8″-5/8″ down vertically as shown. (See fig. 6.1g.)

NOTE:
Brick-like formation partings will conceal all partings of the previous row of individual braid extensions, giving an all-braided look as shown. (See fig. 6.1h.)

How to Apply Individual Braid Extensions

In braid extension and regular hair service, you eventually learn to be ambidextrous. Therefore, to make it possible to follow directions and repeat directions, the text will give instructions for all partings and braids starting at the left and finishing on the right. In applying braid extensions and braiding-down braids, both your right and left hand will have to be equally nimble.

After parting a single individual braid extension as shown in the first section (How to Make Partings for Individual Braid Extensions), it is time to apply the additional hair to create an undetectable individual braid extension. (See fig. 6.2a.)

▲ Separate that portion that is parted out for an individual braid extension into two equal portions as shown. (See fig. 6.2b.)

▲ Hold left portion of hair with left index finger and thumb at base of hair, holding hair straight up. (See fig. 6.2c.)

6.2a Partings for an individual braid extension have been made.

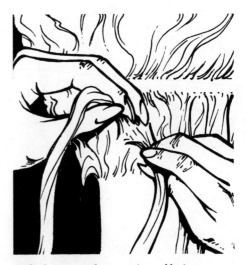

6.2b Separate that portion of hair.

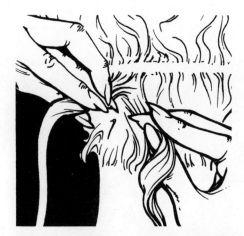

6.2c Hold left portion of hair with left index finger and thumb, and right portion of hair with right index finger and thumb.

6.2d Replace thumb and index finger of left portion of hair . . . filling thumb and index finger.

6.2e Place additional hair between free thumb and index finger of left hand . . . and position right hand.

6.2f Overlap the left portion of client's own hair over the left portion of the additional hair.

▲ The right portion of hair is held with right index finger and thumb, while middle finger is placed directly next to index finger, pressing and directing base of that portion of hair as shown. (See fig. 6.2c.)

▲ Then replace thumb and index fingers holding the left portion of hair with ring and middle finger, freeing thumb and index finger as shown. (See fig. 6.2d.)

▲ Now totally release right portion of hair, freeing right hand to pick up additional hair at its center or at a position that will give the desired length. Place additional hair between free thumb and index finger of the left hand as shown. (See fig. 6.2e.)

▲ Now retain the original position of right hand as instructed before.

▲ Overlap the left portion of client's own hair over the left portion of the additional hair. (See fig. 6.2f.)

6.2g Right portion of client's hair and right portion of additional hair are now combined to form new right portion.

6.2h Now overlap left portion over center.

▲ Additional hair now becomes the new left portion, while the client's left portion of hair becomes the new center.

▲ Right portion of client's hair and right portion of additional hair are now combined to form right portion as shown. (See fig. 6.2g.)

▲ Now take this union of hair and overlap it over center portion to become the new center.

▲ Now overlap left portion over center to make new center, as previous center becomes new left portion. (See fig. 6.2h.)

▲ The additional hair has been applied undetectably, and there are now three portions of hair needed for braiding: the left portion, the center portion, and the right portion. (See fig. 6.2i.)

▲ Continue alternately overlapping left and right portions of hair over the center portion of hair (called overhand braiding). For maximum control over braid work, a slight repositioning of hand and fingers is needed to continue braiding down braid to the end.

▲ Hands and fingers are positioned as shown, with the index finger supporting the braid as it is being formed (alternately). (See fig. 6.2j.)

▲ Left portion of hair overlaps center portion to become new center as previous center goes up to become new left

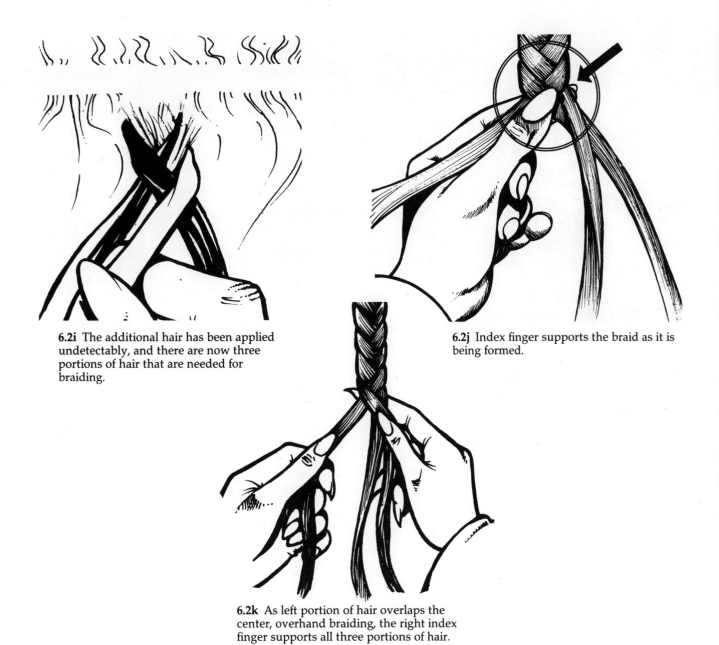

6.2i The additional hair has been applied undetectably, and there are now three portions of hair that are needed for braiding.

6.2j Index finger supports the braid as it is being formed.

6.2k As left portion of hair overlaps the center, overhand braiding, the right index finger supports all three portions of hair.

portion. At the same time, right index finger supports all three portions of hair resting on it, while right thumb presses the new middle portion of hair against right index finger and holds new center in place for left portion to now overlap it. (See fig. 6.2k.)

▲ Right portion of hair overlaps center portion to become new center as previous center goes up to become new right portion. At the same time, left index finger supports all three portions of hair resting on it, while left thumb presses the new middle portion of hair against the left index finger. Then overlap right over center.

▲ Repeat alternately.

Continue to overlap left and right portions of hair alternately over center about 1/8" or more down the braid or until additional hair has been properly reinforced. Then switch to underhand braiding by turning braid over to put underside of braid on top. Left portion now becomes right portion and right portion becomes left portion, as shown. (See fig. 6.2m.)

▲ For underhand braiding, right portion of hair is placed under center portion to become new center.

▲ Now left portion of hair is placed under the center portion to become new center.

▲ Note that palms of hands are facing upward when doing the underhand braid technique, in contrast to overhand braid technique in which palms of hands face downwards.

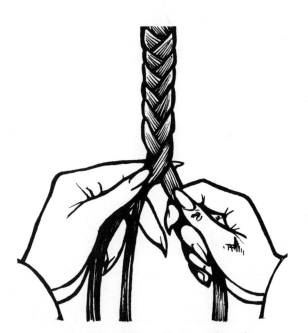

6.2l As right portion of hair overlaps the center, overhand braiding, the left index finger supports all three portions of hair.

6.2m Switch to underhand braiding by turning braid over where the underside of braid is now on top.

How to Make Partings for Cornrow Braid Extension Styles

Precision in partings for cornrow braid extensions is a **must.** Unlike individual braids in which the above row of braids conceals the partings of the previous row, cornrow braid extensions are left on their own to beautify themselves, making it necessary to have precision in partings. (To conceal the partings of a cornrow, they should be made very close to the preceding braided cornrow.)

FOR STRAIGHT PARTS:
Hold tail comb with its metal end pointing downward at a 45° angle, as shown, from client's scalp where part is desired. (See fig. 6.3a.)

▲ Comb will gradually slant in the opposite direction of part at about a 30° angle from scalp, as shown. (See fig. 6.3b.)

▲ Continue parting straight down or straight across as desired without lifting comb from client's scalp.

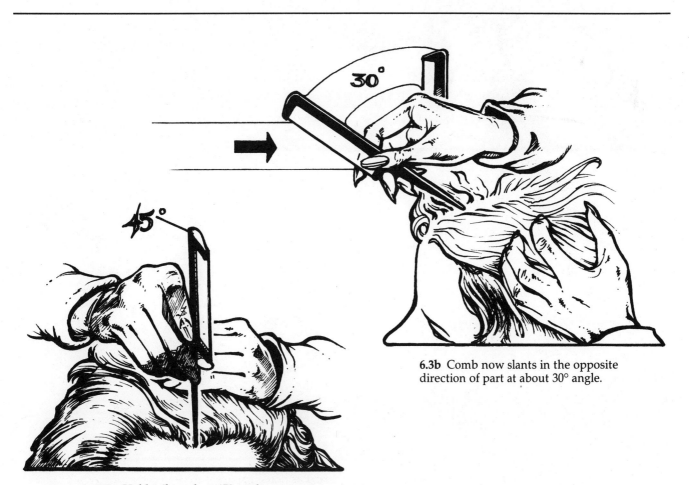

6.3b Comb now slants in the opposite direction of part at about 30° angle.

6.3a Hold tail comb at 45° angle.

FOR DIAGONAL PARTS:

Begin by holding tail comb with its metal end pointing downward at a 45° angle on client's scalp. (See fig. 6.3c.)

▲ Then position wrist in the desired angle for part. (See fig. 6.3d.)

▲ Comb is now slanted in the opposite direction of part about 30°.

▲ Continue parting down at a slanted angle with the tail end of comb remaining on client's scalp at all times.

6.3c Hold tail comb at 45° angle.

6.3d Position wrist in the desired angle for part.

FOR CIRCULAR PARTS:

All parts for braid extensions are straight part; even a precise circular part includes all straight parts.

▲ Begin at desired starting point with metal end of tail comb positioned at 45° angle from client's scalp.

▲ As comb slants about 30°, continue parting horizontally across to desired stopping point without lifting comb. (See fig. 6.3e.)

▲ Then comb portions of hair not needed for immediate use out of the way and secure them with a butterfly clip or clips. **Note:** This can be done after each parting if needed.

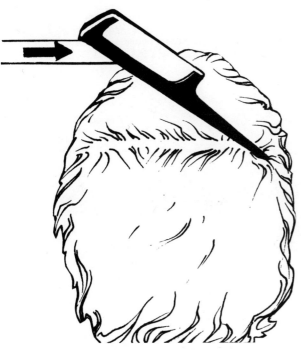

6.3e Position comb at a 45° angle and as comb slants about 30°, continue parting horizontally across.

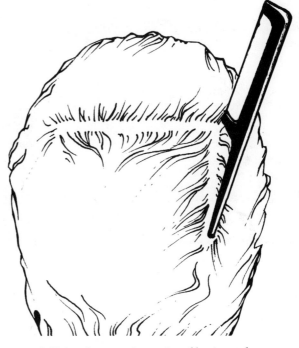

6.3f Using the stopping point of horizontal part as guidepoint...make vertical part.

▲ Using the stopping point of the first horizontal part as a guide point, position comb as instructed before to make vertical point as shown. (See fig. 6.3f.)

▲ Now use the stopping point of the first vertical part as a guide point. Position comb as instructed and make second horizontal part parallel to the first horizontal part, as shown.

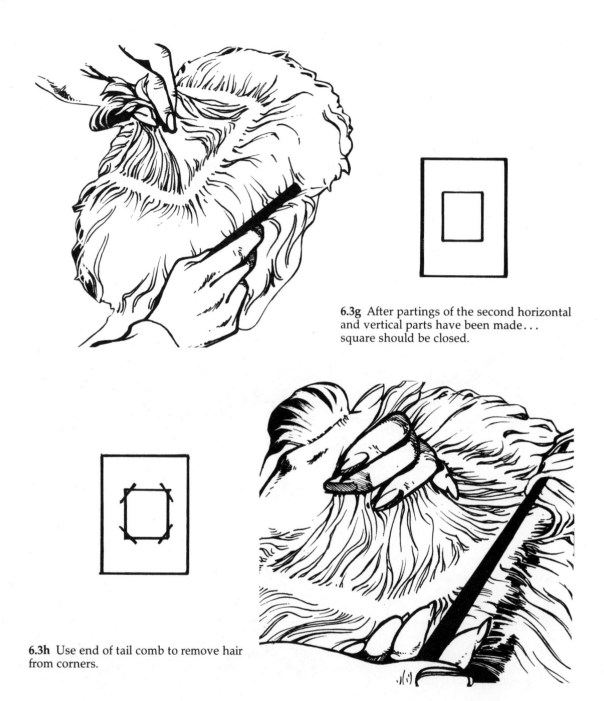

6.3g After partings of the second horizontal and vertical parts have been made... square should be closed.

6.3h Use end of tail comb to remove hair from corners.

▲ Using the starting point of the first horizontal part as a guide point, position comb as instructed and make second vertical part meet stopping point of second horizontal part, closing square. (See fig. 6.3g.)

▲ The end of tail comb can then be used to remove hair from corners, as shown. (See fig. 6.3h.)

▲ End results. (See fig. 6.3i.)

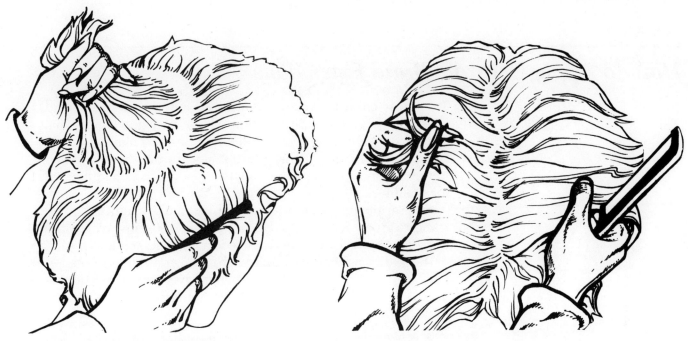

6.3i End results will give circular part.

6.3j Proportional zigzag vertical part.

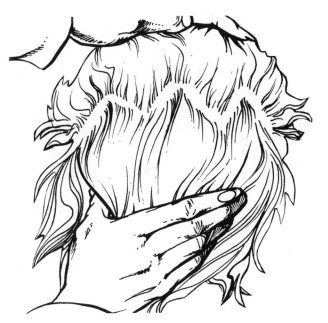

6.3k Proportional zigzag horizontal part.

FOR ZIG ZAG PARTS:
Follow directions given for diagonal parts, using discretion as to the length of each part needed to create proportionate patterns. (See figs. 6.3j and 6.3k.)

How to Apply Cornrow Braid Extensions

To apply cornrow braid extensions, follow directions and illustrations given in the section, "How to Apply Individual Braid Extensions", and follow all directions and illustrations to the point where ..."the additional hair has been applied undetectably, and there are now three portions of hair needed for braiding..."

After applying the additional hair using directions and illustrations given for the individual braid extension—where the overhand-braid technique produced an undetectable application of the additional hair (a couple or more overlappings of the left and right portions of hair alternately over center portion)—switch to the underhand braid technique to make a cornrow braid.

▲ Now switch from overhand to underhand braid as shown, by overlapping left portion of hair over and past center and right portion. Left portion then becomes new right portion, right portion becomes new center, and center is now new left portion. (See fig. 6.4a.)

▲ After the switch, the position is now as illustrated, where center portion is held with index finger and thumb of left hand. (See fig. 6.4b.)

6.4a Make switch from overhand to underhand braid by overlapping left portion of hair over.

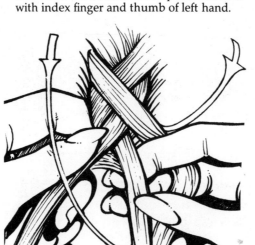

6.4b After the switch, center portion is held with index finger and thumb of left hand.

6.4c Hold right portion of hair and with free right index finger and thumb, reach under center portion of hair to grasp the left portion of hair along with client's hair.

▲ Left portion of hair rests on ring finger of left hand while middle finger secures hair.

▲ Right portion of hair is held with index finger and thumb of right hand.

▲ Raise center portion of hair that is being held up with left index finger and thumb.

▲ Hold right portion of hair between ring and middle finger, freeing index finger and thumb of that hand to reach under center portion of hair to grasp left portion along with a small portion of client's hair, picking it up from the scalp, as shown. (See fig. 6.4c.)

▲ Now raise center portion of hair that is being held with right index finger and thumb up.

▲ Hold left portion of hair between ring and middle finger, freeing index finger and thumb of that hand to reach under center portion of hair to grasp right portion along with a small portion of client's hair, picking it up from scalp, as shown. (See fig. 6.4d.)

▲ Repeat alternately until cornrow braid extensions are completed. (See fig. 6.4e.)

Fingers are always held close to the client's scalp to obtain maximum control over braid work, since cornrowing requires picking up client's hair at base of scalp all during the cornrow braid extension.

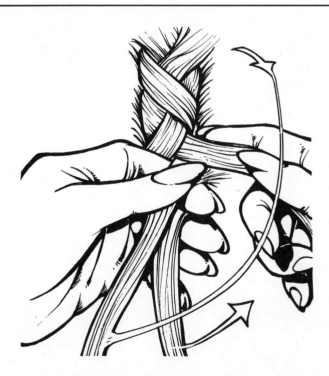

6.4d Hold left portion of hair and with free left index finger and thumb reach under center portion of hair to grasp the right portion of hair along with client's hair.

6.4e Example of a completed cornrow braid extension style.

How to Feed In Extra Additional Hair to the Individual Braid Extension

When braiding individual braid extensions, an occasional problem might arise with a client whose hair is thick and short. The upper portion of the braid combining the client's hair and initial additional hair is much larger than the lower portion, which now includes only additional hair and client hair. This problem can be corrected by feeding in extra additional hair to achieve uniformity.

The art of feeding in extra additional hair should only be used on individual braid extensions braided all the way down to the end. It should not be used on partially braided down styles (invisible braid extensions) because of the risk of losing or pulling out extra additional hair not applied at the base of the client's scalp.

6.5a Braid before extra additional hair has been added.

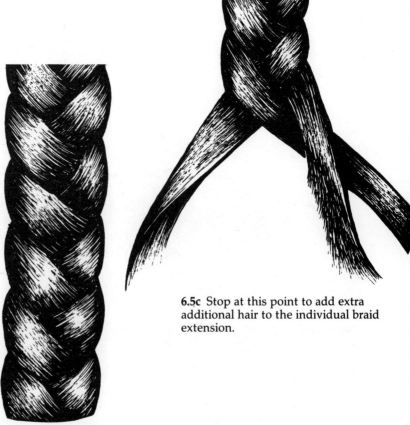

6.5c Stop at this point to add extra additional hair to the individual braid extension.

6.5b Braid before extra additional hair has been added.

The extra additional hair does not have as much holding power as the initial additional hair, the foundation of the braid extension.

▲ Shown—braid without extra additional hair. (See fig. 6.5a.)

▲ Shown—braid after extra addition has been added. (See fig. 6.5b.)

▲ At the point the initial application of additional hair has been added and extra additional hair is now needed. (See fig. 6.5c.)

▲ Support base of forming braid on left index finger while left thumb presses center portion of hair against index finger as shown. (See fig. 6.5d.)

▲ Right portion of hair and right hand are left free.

▲ With free right hand, take up extra additional hair and place it diagonally on top of center portion as shown. (See fig. 6.5e.)

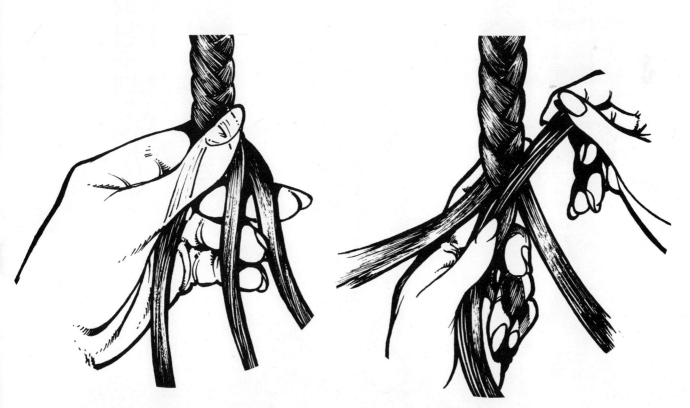

6.5d Support base of forming braid on left index finger and press the center portion of hair with left thumb.

6.5e Place extra additional hair.

▲ Left end of extra additional hair now combines with center portion to form new center portion—as right end of the extra additional hair combines with right portion to form new right portion as shown. (See fig. 6.5f.)

▲ Now overlap left portion of hair over center as center goes up to form new left portion. (See fig. 6.5g.)

▲ Overlap right portion of hair over center so center goes up to form new right portion. (See fig. 6.5h.)

▲ Continue to braid overhand, or switch to the underhand braid as shown in the section "How to Apply Individual Braid Extensions.

Note that to create a set pattern that can be repeated without any confusion, always end with the right portion overlapping to create the center portion before the extra additional hair is applied.

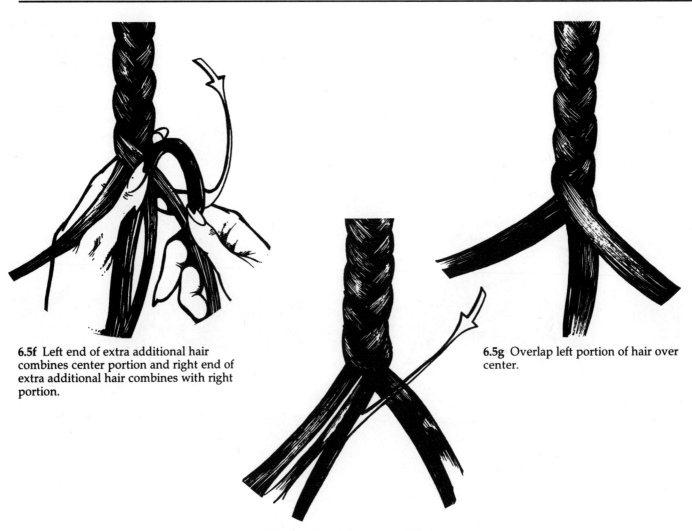

6.5f Left end of extra additional hair combines center portion and right end of extra additional hair combines with right portion.

6.5g Overlap left portion of hair over center.

6.5h Overlap right portion of hair over center.

How to Feed in Extra Additional Hair to the Cornrow Braid Extensions

If larger cornrows are desired for a style—for example, cornrows 1/4″ to 1/2″ wide—do not try to apply such amounts of additional hair at one time. The added weight and pressure would be too much for your client's hair, which could break off at the beginning of the cornrow braid extension. Also, the excessive amounts of additional hair would produce a detectable braid extension.

To prevent the client's own hair from breaking off at the beginning of the extension, and to create an undetectable extension for the process of adding more additional hair, the extra additional hair should be added in gradually. This gradual adding of extra additional hair can be repeated as often as needed until the desired width of braid is achieved.

▲ Follow all directions and illustrations in figs. 6.4a—6.4e, for feeding in extra additional hair.

▲ To the point "... Hold left portion of hair between ring and middle finger, freeing index finger and thumb of that hand to reach under center portion of hair to grasp right portion along with a small portion of client's hair, picking it up from scalp as shown." (See fig. 6.6a.)

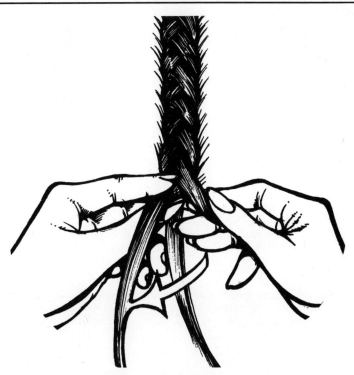

6.6a Stop at this point to add extra additional hair to cornrow braid.

▲ Now release right portion of hair, freeing right hand to pick up extra additional hair and place it diagonally on top of center portion which is now under the right portion, as shown.

▲ Note left end of extra additional hair is now combined with center portion, and right end of extra additional hair is combined with right portion. (See fig. 6.6b.)

▲ Use free right hand to hold combined right portion of hair and right end of extra additional hair with middle and ring fingers.

▲ The now free right index finger and thumb reach under center portion to grasp left portion, along with a small portion of client's hair picked up from scalp to become new center portion.

▲ Applying extra additional hair can be repeated as often as needed. (See fig. 6.6c.)

6.6b Left end of extra additional hair combines with center portion, and right end of extra additional hair combines with right portion of hair.

6.6c The application of extra additional hair can be repeated as needed to obtain a more proportional cornrow braid.

How to Braid Invisible Braid Extensions

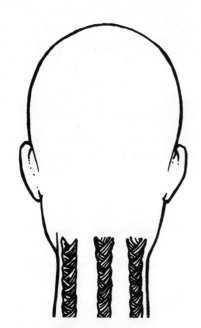

6.7a Braid first layer of braids down about 6/8th of braid.

6.7b Braid second layer of braids down about 5/8th of braid.

To review what has been covered in this chapter, you have learned how to do individual braid extensions, braiding down all the way with the overhand or underhand technique. The importance of the brick-like formation partings concealing all partings of the previous row of individual braid extensions to give an all braid look was also stressed. The art of feeding in extra additional hair for a more proportionate individual braid was explained and illustrated, but is to be used only if needed. How to do precise partings for the cornrow braid extension, how to apply cornrow braid extensions, and how to feed in additional hair to get a larger cornrow were also taught.

Invisible braid extensions that are simply individual braids not braided down to the ends use the same brick-like partings to conceal parts from the previous row of braid extensions, but feeding in extra additional hair is **not** part of this procedure. Extra additional hair should not be added to the invisible braid extension, since such an extension braid is not braided down to the ends of braids. Extra additional hair slides out if added to the invisible braid extension.

Invisible braid extensions on straight, curly or tightly curled hair differ in how far down the braid extensions are braided before the loose ends without the initial additional hair sliding out. For example, braid extensions are braided farther down for clients with straight hair, and not as far down for clients with curly hair. Tightly curled hair is braided down the least of all three types. Not only does the invisible extension have to be braided down more on the client with straight hair, reinforcement is also needed for the top layer of braids. Sometimes the layer of braids directly under the top layer of braids might need to be reinforced as well (as illustrated). For clients with curly hair, reinforcement is generally needed only for the top layer of hair, and no reinforcement is needed for clients with tightly curled hair.

For clients with straight hair:

▲ As shown, braid first layer of braids down about 6/8 of braid. (See fig. 6.7a.)

▲ Braid second layer of braids down about 5/8th of braid as shown. (See fig. 6.7b.)

▲ Braid third layer of braids down about 4/8th of braid as shown. (See fig. 6.7c.)

▲ The braid work will now look like this. (See fig. 6.7d.)

As the braiding process proceeds upward, each successive layer is braided down 1/8th less than the previous layer (e.g., the first layer is braided down 6/8" of braid, the second layer 1/8th less than the first layer and the third layer 1/8th less than the second layer).

Note that instruction given for the client with straight hair also applies to the client with chemically straightened hair.

▲ After completing top layer of braids—braids should be reinforced as shown with weaving needle and thread (thread should be same color as client's hair or as close as possible), or by other appropriate means of reinforcing. Reinforcing the layer directly under the top layer of braids might also be needed. (See fig. 6.7e.)

▲ Finally, client's own hair is combed over top layer of reinforced braids, resulting in one continuous loose looking hair style as shown. But note that additional hair used can be curly, wavy, etc., or various curl or wave formations can be achieved by setting or using electrical devices for such purposes. (See fig. 6.7f.)

▲ For clients with curly hair, braid first layer of braids down about 5/8th of braid, the second layer of braid down about 4/8th of braid, and the third layer of braid down about 4/8th of braid.

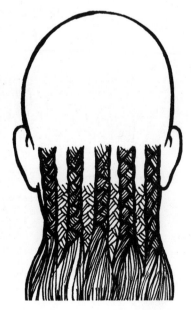

6.7c Braid third layer of braid down about 4/8th of braid.

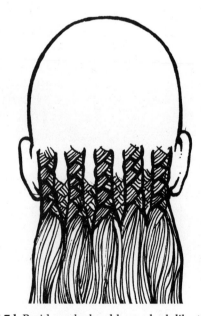

6.7d Braid work should now look like this.

▲ Use instructions and illustrations given for the client with straight hair—and keep in mind that the only difference so far in the procedure is that the client with curly hair braids has braids that are braided down a fraction less than the client with straight hair.

▲ After the top layer of braids has been completed, it should be reinforced as instructed for the client with straight hair.

▲ Finally, the client's own hair is combed over top layer of reinforced braids, resulting in one continuous loose looking style as shown. But note that additional hair used **can be straight if desired.**

▲ For clients with tightly curled hair, braid first layer of braids down about 4/8th of braid, the second layer of braids down about 3/8th of braid, and the third layer of braids down about 2/8th of braid.

▲ Use instructions and illustrations given for the client with straight hair, but keep in mind that the tightly curled hair is braided down the least.

▲ **Note:** For clients with tightly curled hair, all the client's hair should be enclosed in braid extension.

▲ Since so little braiding down is needed, the final result will be one continuous loose-looking hair style, as shown.

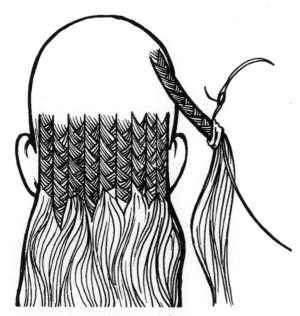

6.7e After top layer of hair has been braided...reinforce.

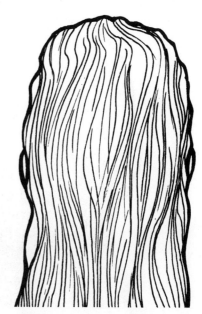

6.7f Client's own hair is then combed over top layer of reinforced braids.

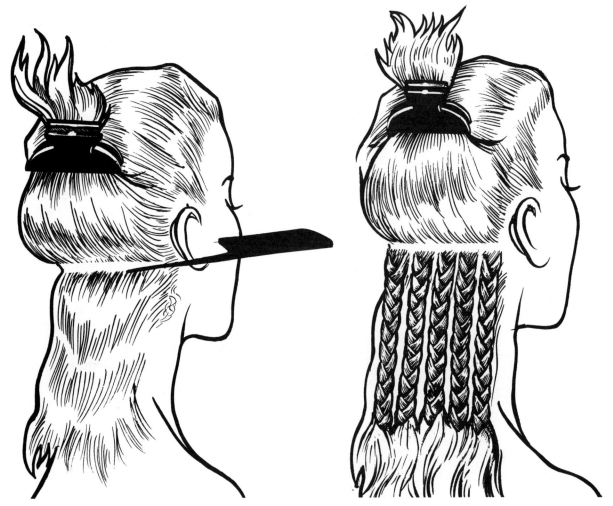

6.7g Part client's hair 1/8 to 5/8 inch from nape.

6.7h Part another 1/8 to 5/8 inch of hair above the previous row, and braid a row of invisible braids.

SPECIAL NOTE:
When braiding invisible braid extensions for clients who are pleased with the length and condition of their naturally straight or curly hair—yet want more body—you can follow the steps given in the section "How To Do Invisible Braid Extensions", with the exception that braid extensions should not be applied to every row but to every other row as shown. Example: 1st row, part client's hair 1/8 to 5/8″ from the nape of client's neck; comb hair down, and secure with butterfly clip (leaving this clipped portion of hair out will enable clients to wear their hair up if they choose without detection of any braid work). (See fig. 6.7g.) 2nd row—next, part another 1/8 to 5/8″ of hair above the previous row (follow directions given in the section "How To Do Invisible Braid Extensions" by braiding a row of invisible braids down. Each braid is braided down as far as 6/8″ from the end of braid). (See fig. 6.7h.) 3rd row—part 1/8 to 5/8″ of client's hair above

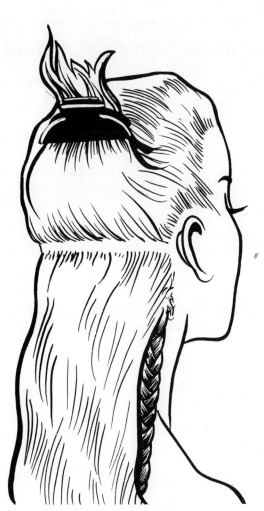

6.7i Part 1/8 to 5/8 inch of client's hair above previous row of braids.

6.7j Continue alternating with a layer of invisible braids and a layer of client's unbraided hair.

previous row of braids. (See fig. 6.7i.) Remove butterfly clip from bottom row, comb third row of client's hair down, and secure with butterfly clip. Keep alternating with a layer of invisible braids and a layer of client's unbraided hair combed down (follow directions given for clients with straight or curly hair, whatever applies. (See fig. 6.7j.)

This technique of alternating rows of invisible braids and combed down unbraided hair gives hair a similar look to that which results from fusing, another hair addition technique (discussed in Chapter 10). With the invisible braiding technique, only additional hair is required and the client has the option of using any type of hair: human, Yak, or synthetic. The fusing technique requires additional hair (synthetic hair only), and a heat conducting tool to melt and fuse the additional hair and client's hair together.

How to Combine Individual and Cornrow Braid Extensions

Combining individual braid extensions with cornrow braid extensions is usually done with the individual braids in the back of the client's head and cornrow braid extensions in the front. The ends of both individual and cornrow braid extensions can be left loose or braided to end of braid if desired.

For cornrows which start at forehead and end midway to client's ear, proceed as follows:

▲ Start individual braid extensions at nape of client's neck and end midway to client's ear, as illustrated. (See fig. 6.8a.)

▲ A variation of this is when both cornrow and individual braid extensions are left loose at end, as illustrated. (See fig. 6.8b.)

For cornrows which start at forehead and end approximately 1"-2" as it approaches the crown of client's head, proceed as follows:

▲ Start individual braid extensions at nape of client's neck and end 1"-2" before reaching client's forehead, as illustrated. (See fig. 6.8c.)

6.8a The finished look of individual braid extension braided from nape to midway of client's ear, then finished with cornrow braid extensions in front. Both individual and cornrow braid extensions are braided to the end of braid.

6.8b Finished look of invisible braid extension braided from nape to midway of client's ear, then finished with cornrow braid extension in front. Both invisible and cornrow braid extensions are left loose at ends.

▲ A variation of this is when both ends of cornrow and individual braid extension are left loose, as illustrated. (See fig. 6.8d.)

Note: Keep in mind that the further back the cornrows are braided (e.g. passed the crown), the flatter the braid style appears.

6.8c The finished look of individual braid extension braided from nape to 1″-2″ before reaching client's forehead, then the front is finished with cornrow braid extension. Both individual and cornrow braid extensions are braided to the end of braid.

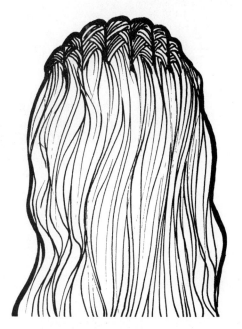

6.8d The finished look of invisible braid extension braided from nape to 1″-2″ before reaching client's forehead, then the front is finished with cornrow braid extensions. Both invisible and cornrow braid extensions are left loose at ends.

How Some Braid Styles Are Affected by the Direction in Which They Are Braided

The direction in which individual braid extensions are applied—especially in creating invisible braid extensions—is very important to achieve height in the front or crown area of client's braid style, as illustrated.

▲ To acquire height in front of client's braid extension style, start at the nape of client's neck and braid invisible braid extension in downward direction, as shown, until stopping point is reached. (See fig. 6.9a.)

6.9a To acquire height in front of braid extension, braid invisible braid extension from nape to stopping point.

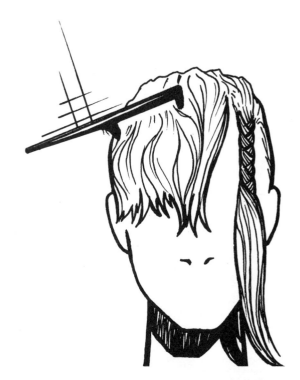

6.9b Turn client around, and braid invisible braid extension 1″-2″ from forehead thus leaving out sufficient amount of client's hair to comb over braids.

▲ After the stopping point has been reached on the back portion of the client's head, turn client around. You are now face to face with client. Start invisible braid extension now from client's forehead or 1″-2″ from forehead, leaving out a sufficient amount of client's hair to be combed over invisible braids. (See fig. 6.9b.)

▲ Finished braid style shows height in the front of client's style. (See fig. 6.9c.)

▲ To acquire height in front and crown of client's braid extension style or just to exaggerate height, start at nape of client's neck and braid invisible braid extension downward until the **new** stopping point is reached, as shown. (See fig. 6.9d.)

▲ After the stopping point has been reached on back portion of the client's head, turn client around. You are now face to face with client. Start invisible braid extension now from client's forehead or 1″-2″ from forehead and continue to stopping point, as shown.

▲ Finished braid style shows height in front and crown of client's braid style.

6.9c Finished braid style should show height in front of client's invisible braid style.

6.9d To acquire height in front and crown of braid extension, braid invisible braid extension from nape to stopping point.

6.9e Finished braid style should show height in front and crown of client's invisible braid style.

The Importance of Good Finger Dexterity and Control Over Braid Extension Work

Finger technique has been explained and illustrated in figs. 6.2, 6.4, 6.5 and 6.6. Therefore, you need only practice and follow these step-by-step explanations and illustrations. With continuous repetition, good finger dexterity and control of braid extension work will become second nature.

One key thing to remember when practicing the illustrated finger techniques of figs. 6.2, 6.4, 6.5 and 6.6 is to keep your fingers close to the base of the forming braid.

Note: Keeping your hands and fingers mobile and relaxed during the lengthy duration of braid extension work is important to obtain maximum performance with ease. To prevent dry, stiff hands from impeding mobility, slowing down braiding and tiring hands, you can apply petroleum jelly to hands and fingers, tissuing off the excess as often as needed during the process.

Simple Braid Extension Work

Two of the simplest braid extension styles are the French Braid and a large cornrow braid done in back of the client's head. These simple yet popular braid styles are usually for clients with long hair, but through the aid of additional hair, clients with short hair can also enjoy these styles without any detection of additional hair.

To achieve these simple braid extension styles, you must practice and master the art of constantly feeding in extra additional hair that these styles demand. Good finger dexterity and control over braid work are essential.

THE LARGE CORNROW BRAID EXTENSION:
First, comb both sides of client's hair toward the center as shown (gel, sprays or their equivalents can be used on sides of client's hair. (See fig. 6.10a.) Then brush sides to hold neatly in place. Second, begin by following the directions in the section, "How to Apply Cornrow Braid Extensions." Follow these directions past the point where the switch from overhand braid to underhand

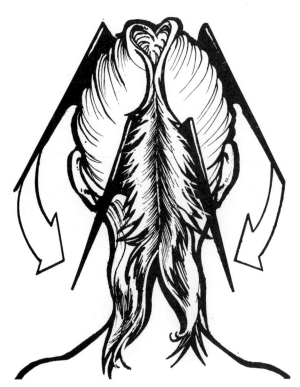

6.10a Comb both sides of client's hair towards the center, and position hair as shown before applying the large cornrow braid extension.

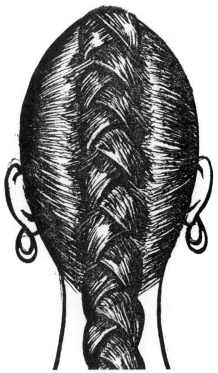

6.10b The finished look of the large cornrow braid extension.

braid is illustrated, to the point where directions read: "...right portion of hair is held with index finger and thumb of right hand..." Stop following directions in the section, "How to Apply Cornrow Braid Extensions," at this point. Third, release right portion of hair, freeing right hand to pick up a substantial amount of extra additional hair (500 or more strands), and place it diagonally on top of center portion of hair as shown. **Note:** Since a larger portion of the client's hair is being used at one time for these simple braid extension styles, client's hair can then accommodate larger portions of additional hair without worrying about the weight or pressure. Fourth, go to the section, "How to Feed in More Additional Hair to the Cornrow Braid Extension." Follow directions starting at, "Now release right portion of hair, freeing right hand to pick up extra additional hair and place it diagonally...." and continue to follow these directions until the end of the procedures in this section.

Note: Extra additional hair should be added at the third step in the procedure. Continue increasing the amount of extra additional hair as the large cornrow braid progresses toward the nape of the client's neck or until the desired width of cornrow is achieved. After cornrowing down to the nape of the client's neck, continue using the underhand braid technique to the end of braid as shown. (See fig. 6.10b.) Hair ornament can be added to the finished hair style if desired.

THE FRENCH BRAID:
Comb both sides of the client's hair toward the center, as in the large cornrow extension. Gels, sprays or their equivalents can be used on the sides of the client's hair. Then brush sides of hair neatly in place. Follow the directions in the section, "How to Apply Cornrow Braid Extensions," but stop following directions before making the switch from overhand braiding to underhand braiding, since you do not need to switch when doing the French braid. The French braid uses the overhand braiding technique throughout the braiding process.

1) Now you should be at this point where the right portion of hair is overlapped to become the new center. 2) Using free right hand, pick up extra additional hair and place it diagonally on the top of center portion of hair as shown. **Note:** The left end of extra additional hair is combined with center portion, and right end of extra additional hair is combined with right portion of hair. 3) Use middle and ring fingers of right hand to hold combined right portion of hair and right end of extra additional hair. 4) With free right index finger and thumb, reach over center portion to grasp left portion of hair along with a small portion of client's hair that is picked up from the scalp to become the new center portion. 5) The combined right portion of hair and small portion of the client's hair picked up from the scalp should now overlap to become new center. 6) The application of extra additional hair

should be repeated at this point and can be repeated as often as needed. 7) After completing the French braid to the nape of client's neck, continue to braid to the end of braid by gently placing right and left portions of hair alternately over center portion of hair as the Franch braid progresses to acquire a continuous French braid look as shown. (See figs. 6.10c and 6.10d.) **Note:** Unlike the large cornrow braid extension, the French braid is an overhand braid. For example, you should reach over, not under, to grasp left or right portions of hair and small portions of client's hair from scalp alternately to form new center. Unlike regular overhand braiding, the French braid does not need much tension. The left and right portions of hair should be gently placed over center portion alternately as if folding, to create a continuous French braid look.

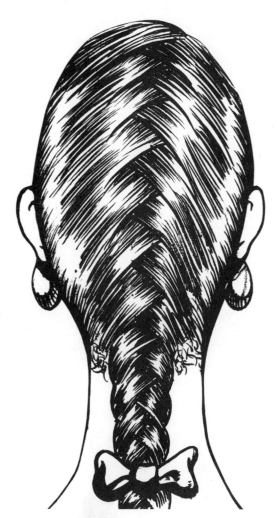

6.10c A finished look of the French braid... braid extension (back view).

6.10d A finished look of the French braid... braid extension (side view).

Intricate Braid Extension Work

Intricate braid extension work can be done using cornrows, partial cornrows and individual braids to create a wide variety of exciting designs.

Intricate braid styles are usually done in up-braid styles, in which the additional hair is normally used for continuous feeding in of hair for proportional braiding, versus other braid styles that use additional hair for length and body.

Having mastered the art of applying undetectable individual and cornrow braid extensions, making precise partings, feeding in extra additional hair, and building good finger dexterity and control, you are ready to start creating as many intricate styles as you can imagine.

▲ Part client's hair in the center of head as shown, roughly 2½" from forehead, 2½" from sides and 2½" from nape, remove corners, then comb hair in front out of the way and secure with clips. (See fig. 6.11a.)

▲ Using tail comb with metal end, part vertically down as shown about 1/2".

▲ Now part diagonally up to left about 1". (See fig. 6.11b.)

▲ Remove hair from corners with end of tail comb.

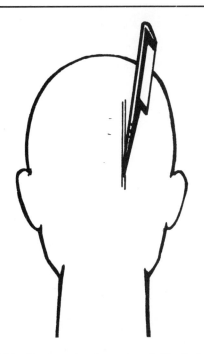

6.11a Start parting in center of client's head.

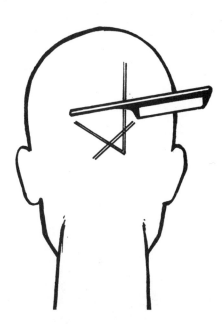

6.11b Part diagonally up to left, then remove hair from corners.

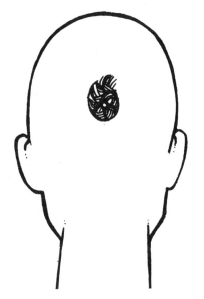

6.11c Cornrow in the additional hair.

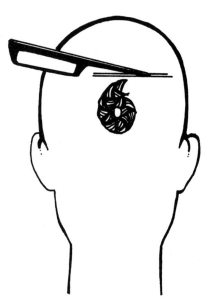

6.11d Part horizontally across.

6.11e Part the next vertical part, and remove corners.

▲ Start cornrowing additional hair in, starting with small amounts of additional hair—and gradually feeding in more hair. Stop cornrow braiding at point indicated. (See fig. 6.11c.)

▲ Part horizontally across as shown. Then part vertical part 1/4″ past horizontal cornrows. (See fig. 6.11d.)

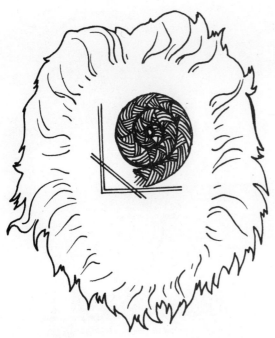

6.11f Cornrow around and alternately repeat partings and removal of corners of both sides.

6.11g Continue cornrowing until center is fully cornrowed with additional hair.

▲ Again remove corner with end of tail comb, and cornrow around, as shown. (See fig. 6.11e.)

▲ Repeat until all hair up to the part has been used. Remove clips from client's hair in front, sides and back as shown. (See fig. 6.11f.)

▲ Center is now fully cornrowed with additional hair and the remainder of client's hair is now ready for the next step. (See fig. 6.11g.)

6.11h Finished back view after hair roll has been rolled in client's hair.

611i Finished front view after hair roll has been rolled in client's hair.

▲ Use hair roll. (Can purchase hair roll or it can be made by stuffing an old stocking).

▲ Place hair roll and roll client's hair in, as shown. (See fig. 6.11h.)

▲ Can leave small portion of client's hair out in front to form tendrils or bangs, if desired. (See fig. 6.11i.)

CHAPTER

7 A PICTORIAL OF BRAID EXTENSION STYLES

The photographs in this chapter show a variety of braid extension styles. They were created using many of the techniques learned in Chapter 6.

The styles are shown from a variety of different angles to give students, cosmetologists and clients a complete perspective. The types of hair used for the various extensions are also included as a guide for determining which types of hair work well for particular styles. These photographs will also give clients a good idea of how certain braid extensions can enhance or change their present hair styles.

7.1a Backview of a combination of visible and invisible braid extension styles (Oriental hair used).

7.1b Front view.

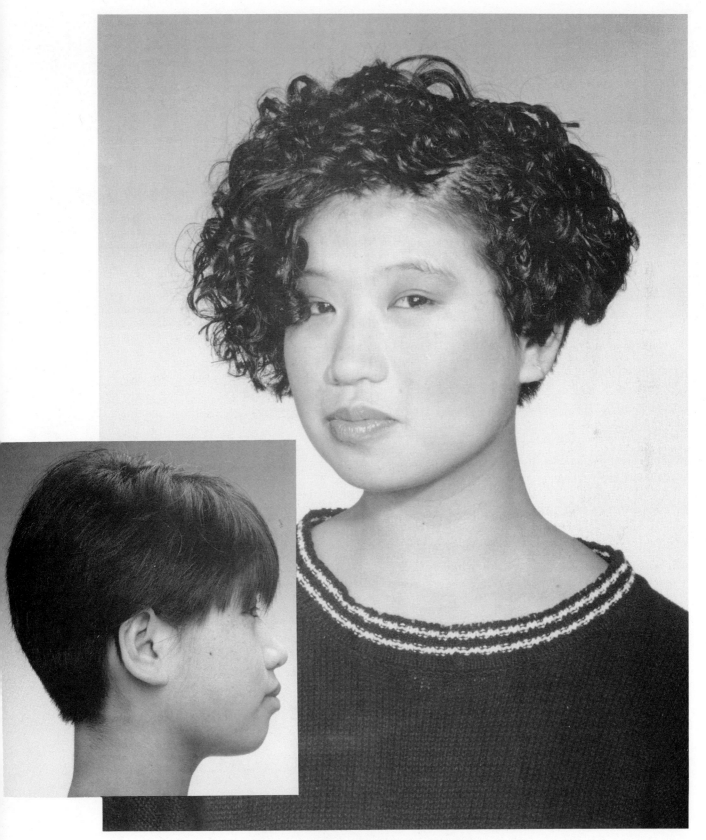

7.2a Before.

7.2b After (with Indian hair used to create this braid extension style).

7.3a Before.

7.3b After (with Yak hair used to create this braid extension style).

7.3c After (with Yak hair used to create another braid extension style).

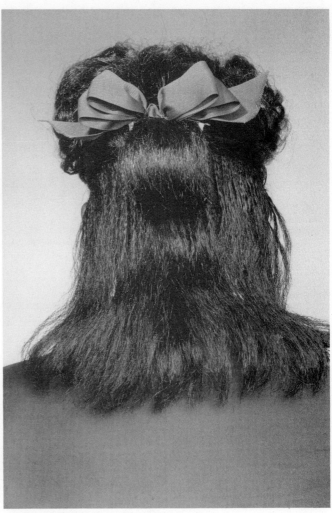

7.4a Front view of a style created from the braid extension shown in fig. 7.3b.

7.4b Back view.

7.5a Back view of large side braid extension style (synthetic hair used).

7.5b Side view.

7.6 Oriental hair used to create braid extension style.

7.7a Front view of braid extension style (Oriental hair used).

7.7b Side view.

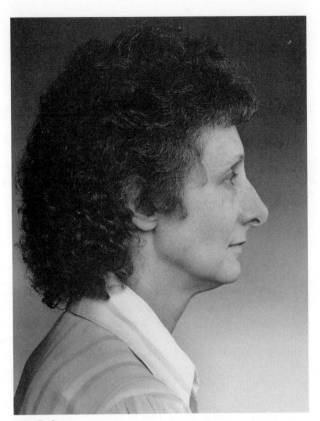

7.8a Before.

7.8b Front view of braid extension style (Oriental hair used). A tight French braid was used since model's hair was short. See French braid technique in Chapter 6.

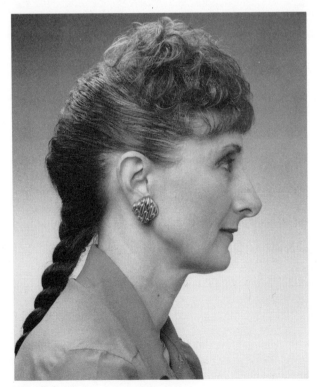

7.8c Side view.

7.8d Back view.

7.9a Side view of cornrow braid extension style created with Oriental hair.

7.9b Back view.

7.10 Two different styles created from one braid extension style.

7.11 Front view of invisible braid extension style (Oriental hair used).

7.12 Braid style created with Oriental hair.

7.13a Front view of braid extension style (Oriental hair used).

7.13b The same braid extension style as it's being blown.

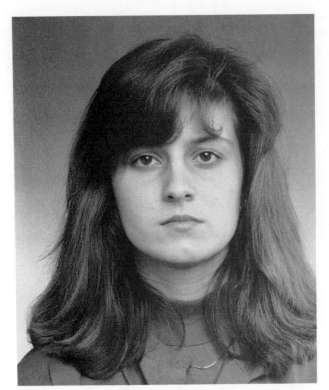

7.14a Front view, before.

7.14b Front view after (with Oriental hair used for this invisible braid extension style). See "Special Note", in Chapter 6, for braid technique used.

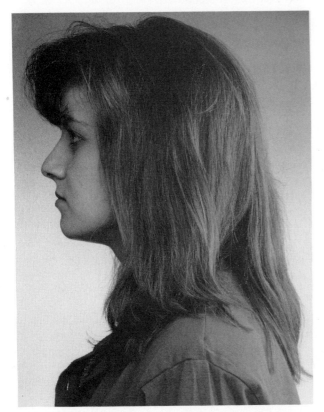

7.14c Side view, before.

7.14d Side view, after.

7.15a Front view, before.

7.15b Front view, after (with Oriental hair used for this braid extension style).

16a Side view, before.

7.16b Side view, after (with Oriental hair used for this braid extension style).

7.16c Front view, after.

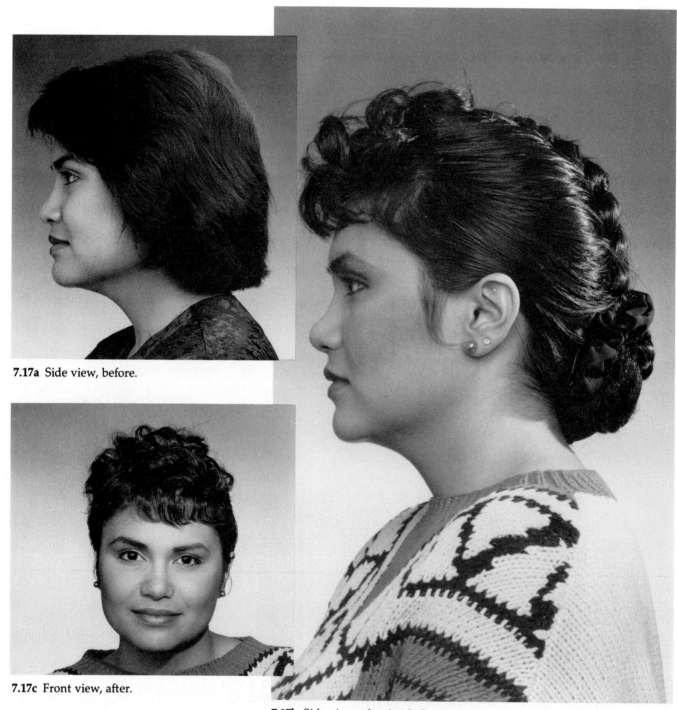

7.17a Side view, before.

7.17c Front view, after.

7.17b Side view, after (with Oriental hair used for this braid extension style).

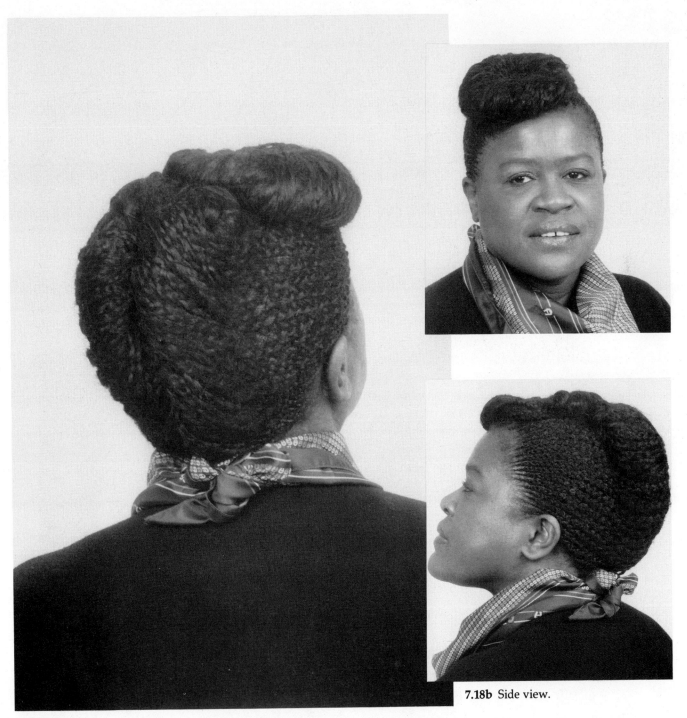

7.18b Side view.

7.18c Back view.

7.19 Braid extension style created with Oriental hair.

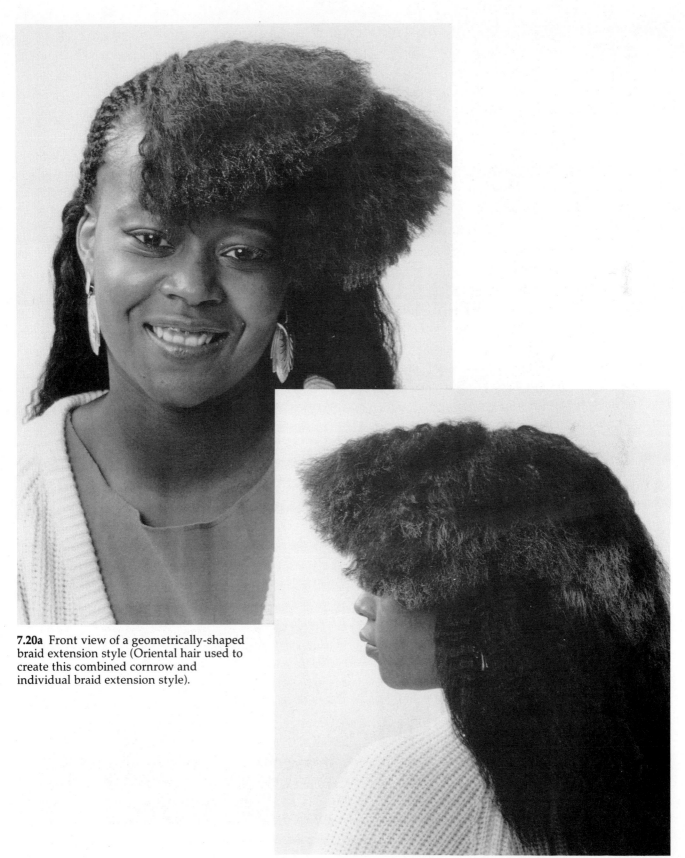

7.20a Front view of a geometrically-shaped braid extension style (Oriental hair used to create this combined cornrow and individual braid extension style).

7.20b Side view.

7.21 Braid style created with Oriental hair.

7.22 Cornrow braid up-style created with Oriental hair.

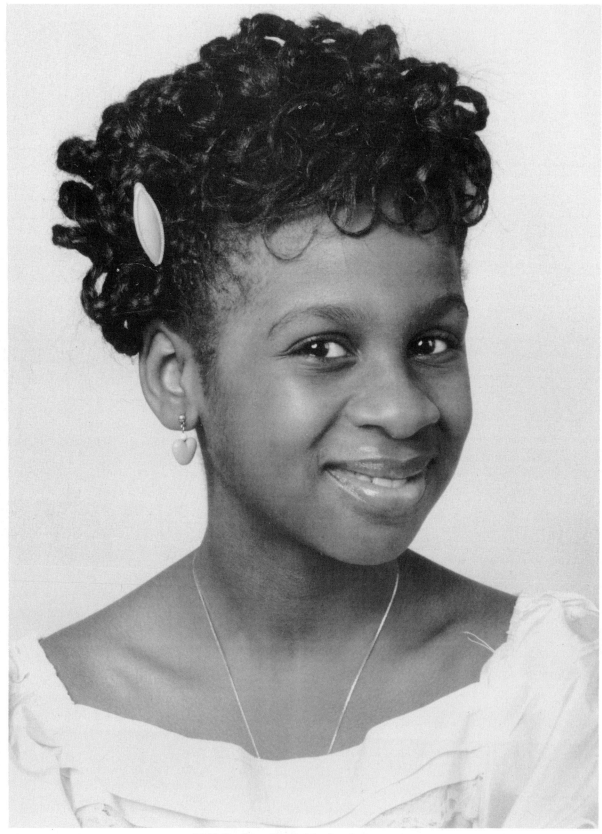

7.23 Combined individual and cornrow braid extension style created with Oriental hair.

7.24a Front view of a braid extension style (Oriental hair used to make braids thicker, and one longer braid of synthetic hair used to wrap braids).

7.24b Side view.

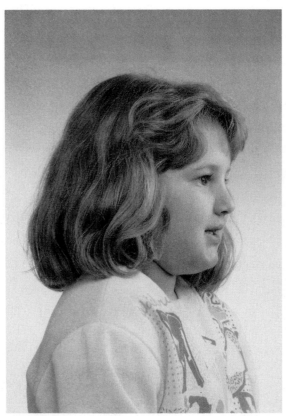

7.25a Before.

7.25b Front view, after (with Oriental hair used for braid extension style).

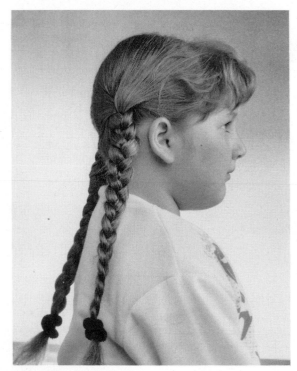

7.25c Side view, after.

7.26a Before.

7.26b After (with Oriental hair used for braid extension style).

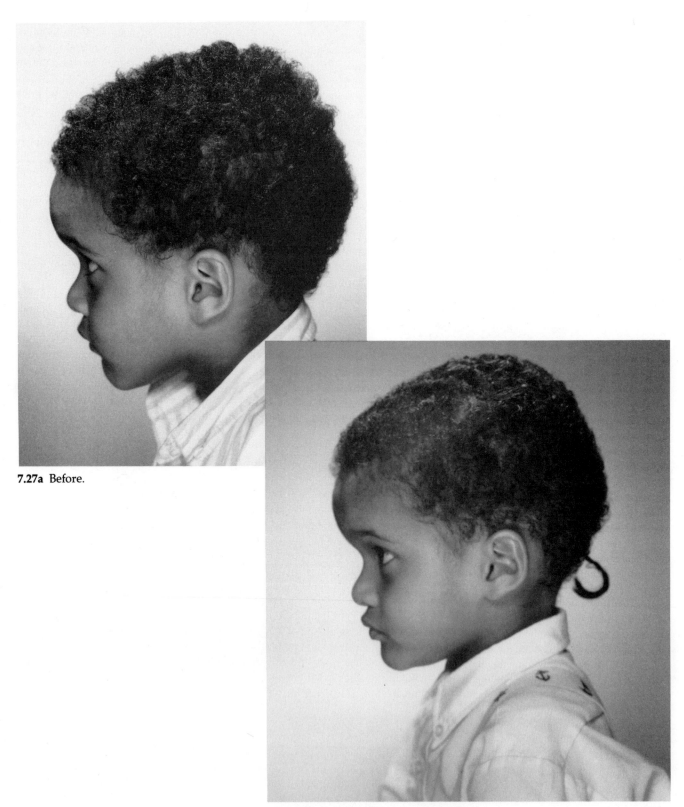

7.27a Before.

7.27b After (with Oriental hair used for braid extension style).

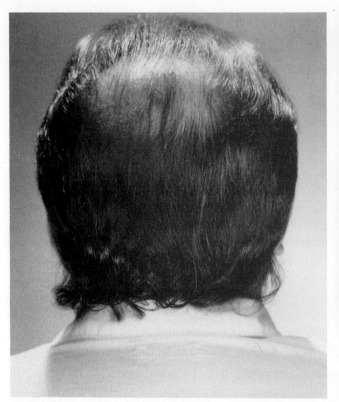

7.28a Before.

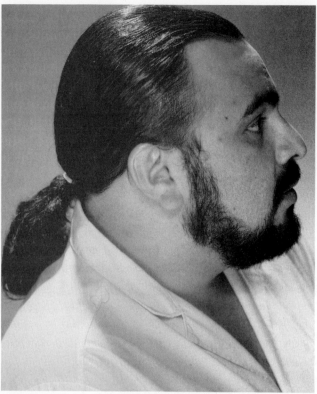

7.28b Side view, after (with Oriental hair used for invisible braid extension to conceal baldness).

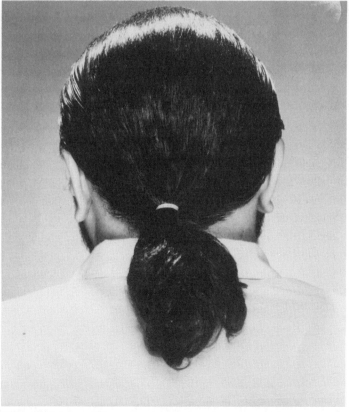

7.28c Back view, after.

7.29 A mixture of Yak and Oriental hair is used to create this braid extension style.

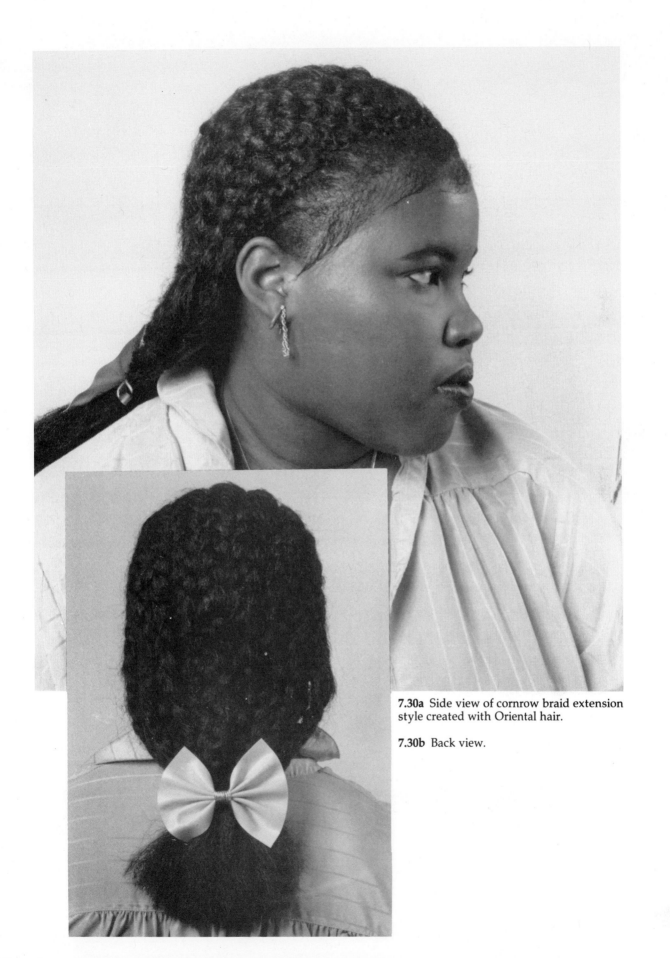

7.30a Side view of cornrow braid extension style created with Oriental hair.

7.30b Back view.

7.31a Front view of braid extension style created with Oriental hair.

7.31b Back view.

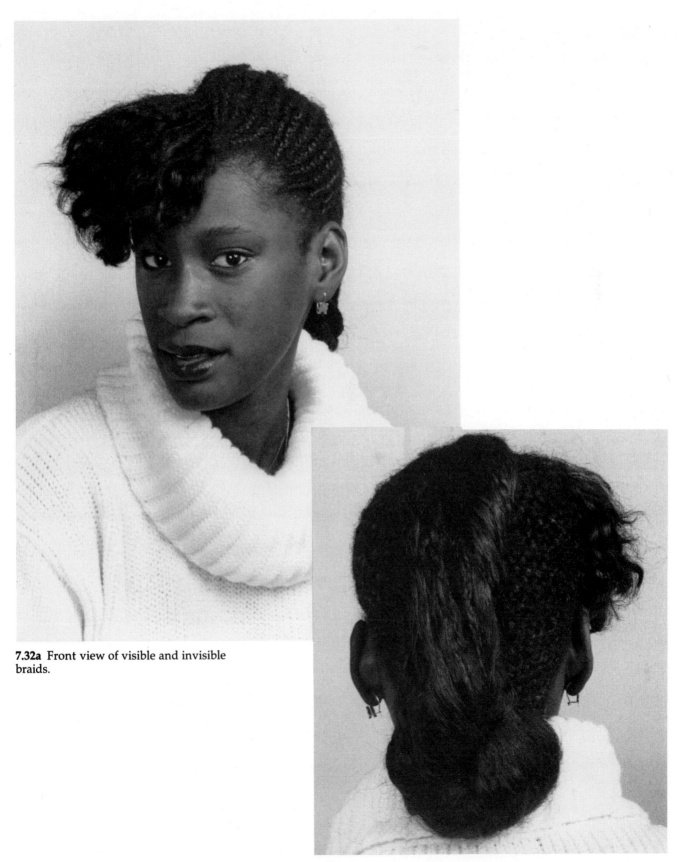

7.32a Front view of visible and invisible braids.

7.32b Back view.

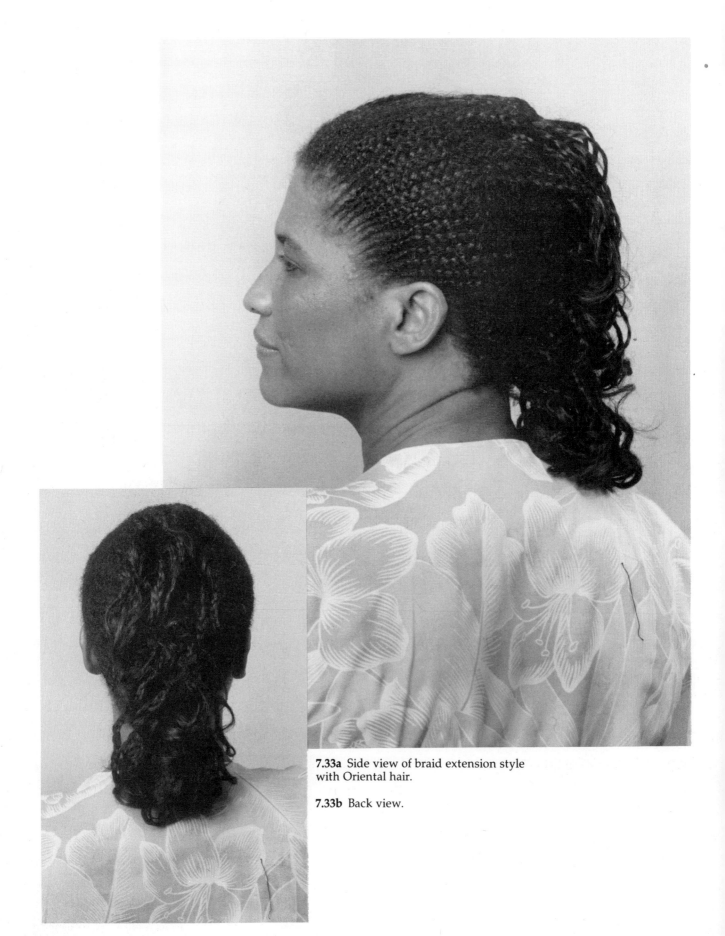

7.33a Side view of braid extension style with Oriental hair.

7.33b Back view.

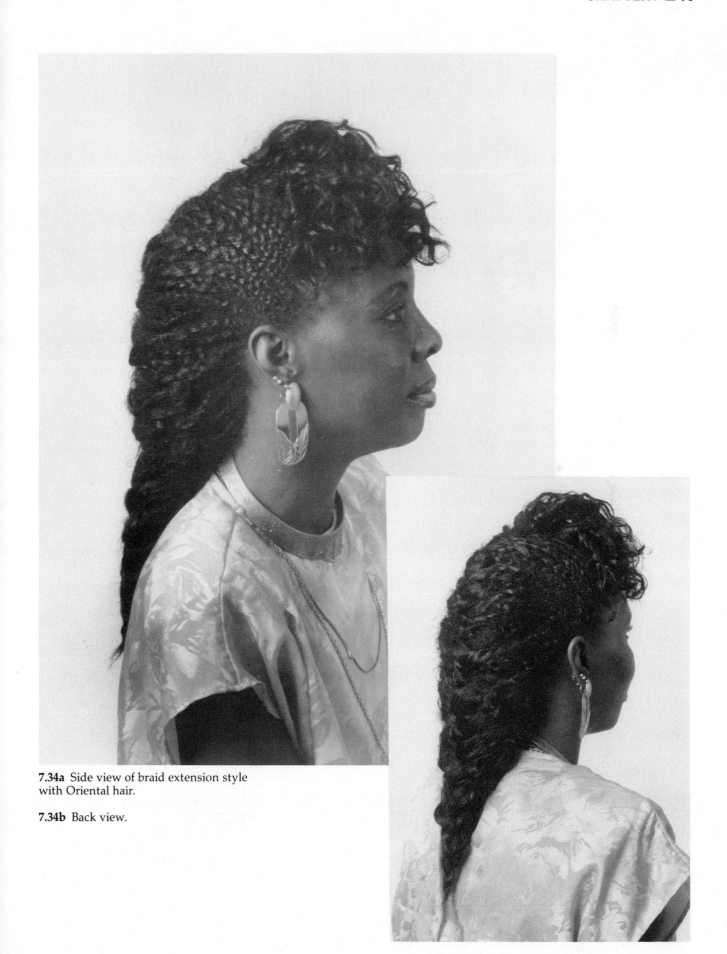

7.34a Side view of braid extension style
with Oriental hair.

7.34b Back view.

7.35a Front view of braid extension style with Oriental hair.

7.35b Back view.

7.36a Before.

7.36b After (with Yak hair used for braid extension style).

7.37a Side view of an intricate braid extension style created with synthetic hair in back and Oriental hair in front.

7.37b Back view.

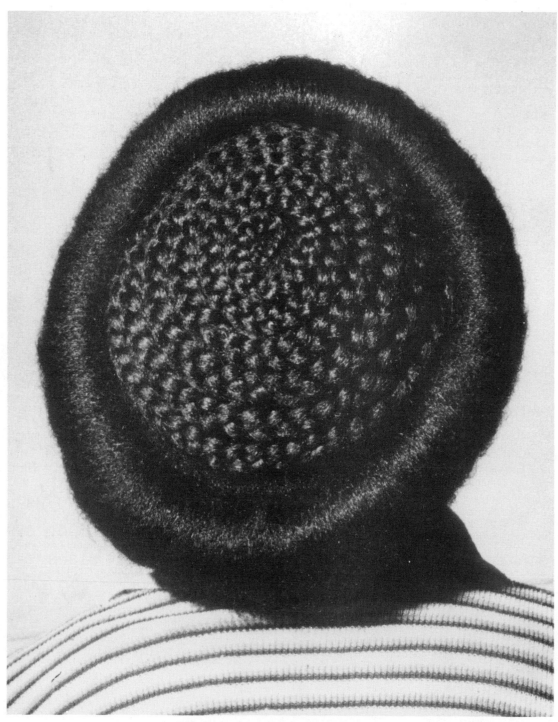

7.38 Back view of intricate braid extension
style with Oriental hair.

7.39a Front view of an intricate style showing the lacing of braid extensions.

7.39b Back view.

CHAPTER

8 HOW TO ELIMINATE SHORT HAIR FROM PROTRUDING OUT OF BRAID EXTENSIONS

You can complete braid extensions for clients with hair of moderate length (four inches or more) with all ends of hair relatively even, without client's hair protruding from the extensions. Protruding hair outside of braid work can be a problem if the client's hair is very short (about an inch or less), if they have had bulk removed from the hair from effilating or thinning shears, or if they have had chemically damaged hair with parts of the shaft dissolved or eaten away.

In this chapter we will discuss possible problems and solutions when dealing with short hair protruding through braid extensions and whether the clients' hair is straight, curly or tightly curled.

Short hair protruding from braid extensions usually does not happen when using small amounts of additional hair for braid extension work and applying individual braid extensions to hair sectioned into very small portions. But when applying cornrow type braid extensions, short hair protruding from braid extensions can be a problem.

How to Eliminate Hair from Protruding from Cornrow-Type Braid Extensions When Working with Clients With Straight, Short Hair

When applying cornrow-type braid extensions on a client with straight, short hair—or whose hair is choppy due to an excessive amount of effilating, or cutting too close to the scalp with thinning shears—simply put a little water, then a small portion of holding gel or its equivalent on the short hair to be held in place. Now apply a little more tension in these areas until they pass the point where the client's hair ends. Continue to braid down the extension until completing the braid. After the braid is done, check the area where more tension had to be applied to make sure it's balanced with the rest of the braid. If the area is not in balance, hold it between your fingers, pressing down with your thumb and pulling the sides of braid slightly outward. The pressing and pulling will help to make the entire braid proportional. Another way is to cut off the ends protruding through the braid extensions. This solution should be used only as a last resort. If the client decides to stop wearing braid extensions, cutting off protruding ends would only result in their hair looking extremely choppy. In most cases, applying water, a small portion of setting gel and added tension will eliminate the problem of straight, short hair protruding from braid extensions.

For Clients with Short Curly Hair—How to Eliminate Short Curly Hair from Protruding Out of Cornrow-Type Braid Extensions

For the client with short curly hair, one and a half inches or less, controlling the short curly ends can be harder than controlling the protruding hair of the client with straight hair. When working with a client whose hair is short and curly, possibly with long and short sections because of effilating or thinning too close to the scalp, it is important to do a test cornrow braid extension on your client during the braid consultation before actually working with the client.

In doing a test cornrow braid extension, the method of applying water, setting gel and adding tension to control short straight hair from protruding should be used on the test braid for short curly hair. If the client's curly hair is thin and fine, this method can be effective. If the client's hair is thick and curly, this method will not work. In that case suggest to your client that a mild perm solution be combed through the hair to get rid of the unruly curl so braiding can proceed without worry of protruding hair. If your client does not want to comply with the use of a permanent solution being combed through the hair, you can recommend they choose other braid styles—like all individual braids or partial braid styles including mostly individual braids and a small portion of cornrow. Again, the last option is to cut off the protruding ends. But as stated before, this option is the least preferred because the hair is left with a choppy, uneven look if the client decides to remove the braid extensions after a short period of time.

For Clients with Short Tightly Curled Hair—How to Eliminate Short Tightly Curled Hair from Protruding Out of Cornrow-Type Extensions

Short and tightly curled hair—with short and long sections due to excessive effilating, thinning too close to the scalp with shears, or chemical damage—is usually easier to braid than short straight or curly hair. In fact, tightly curled hair an inch or less long can be braided with no problem since it tends to hug and loop the additional hair with its tight curl.

However, if the tightly curled hair protrudes from the cornrow-type braid extensions, it can give an untidy, fuzzy appearance after a while. Short hair protruding from braid extensions usually does not happen if the braid extensions are individual braids with small sections of client's hair and small portions of additional hair. To correct the problem of tight curly hair protruding from the cornrow-type braid extension style, recommend that your client choose an individual braid style or a partially individual and cornrowed style, with the greater portion of the style braided with individual braids. This is because each layer of individual braids overlaps and hides the previous layer, reducing the visibility of any hair protruding out of the extension. If hair is to be braided into a continuous cornrow extension, there is the problem of hair protruding from the scalp area, sticking out of the braid extension and making the work look fuzzy and disorderly. Your client may insist on cornrow braid extension styles after you recommend individual or partial individual and cornrow styles. Suggest the hair be relaxed with a relaxer whose main reagent is ammonium bisulfate, which frees the hair of its tight curl, making it smoother and more manageable. Then proceed with cornrow braid extensions without fear of unruly fuzziness. If your client does not want a relaxer, resort to the last option of cutting off protruding ends.

In summary, note that for short protruding hair—whether naturally short or uneven due to effilating, thinning too close to the scalp or chemical damage—it is best to first recommend that your client choose individual braids or partial individual and cornrow styles instead of totally cornrowed braided styles. For the client with straight hair, water and holding gel can be applied to hair to prevent the ends from sticking out. For the client with curly hair, a mild permanent solution can be combed through the hair to eliminate protruding short hair before braid extension work is done. For tightly curled hair protruding from cornrow braid extensions, relaxing with ammonium bisulfate as the main reagent can be used before braid extension work to control the unruly curled hair from fuzzing over the braid extension. Remember, the last option to be used—whether the hair is straight, curly or tightly curled—is cutting off the protruding ends, since your clients' own hair will look choppy if they stop wearing braid extensions.

CHAPTER

9 HOW TO CARE FOR AND MAINTAIN BRAID EXTENSIONS

Braid extension styles can last from one week to two months. The proper care and maintenance of your clients' braid extensions are vital for a neat appearance and a clean, healthy scalp. You should inform clients beforehand that although maintenance service is provided for the upkeep of the clients' braid extensions, they themselves must take responsibility for some maintenance of their braid extensions. This chapter is divided into two parts. Part I is titled: "The Students' and Cosmetologists' Responsibility for the Care and Maintenance of the Clients' Braid Extensions." Part II is titled "Clients' Responsibility for the Care and Maintenance of Their Braid Extensions." This part should be used as a guide to instruct your clients how to maintain their braid extension styles.

Students' and Cosmetologists' Responsibility for the Care and Maintenance of the Client's Braid Extensions

Let's start with the care and maintenance of very simple braid extension styles like French braids or large cornrow extension styles as shown in Chapter 6, 6-11. Simple styles like these do not last as long or cost as much as more time-consuming styles. Your client should have the entire braid style rebraided anew, since these styles take minutes instead of hours. These simple styles can last from five days to two weeks, with minimum care on the client's part. To care for these simple styles, you should first remove the additional hair from the client's hair and follow these procedures on how to clean it.

If the removed additional hair is Oriental, European, Indian or Yak, follow these directions.

1) Get a large bowl or basin, shampoo and conditioner. 2) Take the additional hair and tie a piece of string around it or knot the additional hair to hold it in place while shampooing and conditioning. 3) Put shampoo in bowl or basin and add very warm water. 4) Soak the additional hair for a few minutes. 5) Squeeze hair several times (this procedure is equivalent to shampooing. 6) Rinse hair properly, making sure tie or knot in hair is still in place. 7) Then condition and blow dry.

If the additional hair that was removed is synthetic hair, use the following procedures: 1) First, get a large bowl or basin, shampoo formulated for synthetic hair, a wig cleaner from a wig shop, and a replenishing conditioner to recapture the body and luster of the synthetic hair. The replenisher can also be purchased from a wig shop. 2) Proceed by using the directions for cleaning human hair.

After preparing your client's additional hair—whether human or synthetic—you should prepare your client's own hair for braid extension work. To do this, see Chapter 5, second paragraph. If clients with simple braid styles come in about once a week to maintain their styles, a shampoo and conditioning mentioned in Chapter 5 will suffice. However, in the third to fourth week a more extreme treatment for your client's scalp and hair can be given. For example, if your client has dandruff, apply a hot oil treatment and massage it into the scalp using the proper manipulation. During the massage you can also use an infrared lamp to warm and relax your client's scalp. Follow the procedure by using the heating cap for 15 to 20 minutes to increase the penetration of the oil treatment. After your client's head has cooled, wash hair with a good cleansing shampoo or special dandruff shampoo if needed. A finishing shampoo with good rinseability can be used. Hair should then be towel dried, sprayed with vitamin or protein infusium and finally blow dried. If your client has no dandruff problem, wash hair with a mild shampoo, then use a good deep penetrating conditioner. The conditioner may be applied to the scalp, and an infrared lamp can be most beneficial during the massage manipulation. A steamer or heating cap can then be used. Allow your client's head to cool, rinse, towel dry, then spray with vitamin or protein infusium and blow dry. **Note:** These instructions on how to prepare your client's hair for braid extension work can be used for all simple braid styles, whether client's hair is straight, curly or tightly curled.

We will now discuss the care and maintenance of more intricate or time-consuming braid extension styles that can last up to two months. Note, however, that braid styles on clients with tightly curled hair usually last longer than those on clients with curly or straight hair. Since these intricate or time-consuming styles can last so long, you must provide a maintenance service for such clients. Charging a moderate price makes it easy for your clients to maintain a continuous neat appearance of their braid extension styles. These maintenance services, called braid touch-ups, can be done one to four weeks after the initial braid work, depending on whether the client's hair is straight, curly or tightly curled. Clients with tightly curled hair can generally go for a longer time before a touch-up is needed.

For the client who needs a braid touch-up one to two weeks after initial braid work, follow these instructions: 1) Do not remove client's braids. 2) Apply a non-peroxide hair and skin antiseptic to cotton or, preferably, gauze squares. (Note: Always use a non-peroxide hair and skin antiseptic to prevent your client's hair from lightening). Use cotton or gauze to clean your client's scalp by removing any accumulated dirt between braids. 3) Wash hair once with a mild shampoo. 4) Condition with an instant conditioner if needed. 5) Dry—slightly. 6) Repeat applying hair or skin antiseptic again if desired to give a nice refreshing feeling. 7) Check braids to make sure they are intact. Proceed to make adjustments to tidy up the braids in front of client's head. The orderly appearance of front braids gives the braid extension work a neat and fresh look. You can make adjustments by removing one braid at a time and rebraiding it neatly back into its original style.

Clients with tightly curled hair usually wear their braid styles for about two months. However, they should be reminded that, although they might find that their braid styles might still look good, keeping the extensions in beyond two months may retard healthy growth. With too much growth in tightly curled hair, it tends to lock together at the roots if braid extensions are left in too long. Your client would be defeating the purpose of enjoying new healthy growth, since some hair loss would happen in removing the locking of hair. If your client needs a touch-up three to four weeks after the initial braid work, follow these procedures for a more extreme treatment: 1) Apply hair and skin antiseptic to cotton or gauze and use this to rub on client's scalp between braids to remove any built-up dirt. 2) A hot oil treatment can be applied to scalp between braids by rubbing oil in gently; use a heating cap for 15 to 20 minutes to help the oil penetrate the scalp. 3) Let the client's head cool, then wash with a good cleansing shampoo and dry lightly. 4) Check braids, making sure they are intact. Tidy up the front of the braid work, if needed, by removing one braid at a time and rebraiding it back immediately. 5) After the touch-up has been completed, rewet the ends of the hair for additional smoothness by spraying on some hot water and then applying some petroleum jelly, followed by a holding spray. Let hair dry naturally.

This process is to be used only if the braid style uses Oriental or Yak hair braided all the way down to the ends. If the braid style was done in Oriental or Yak hair with the ends left loose, dry hair and curl electrically. If the Oriental hair has been processed to obtain a permanent curl formation, respray hair with additional water, brush with a good plastic blow drying brush, and the curls will reappear. If more curl or luster is needed, apply an appropriate curl activator for this purpose. If crimping or waving is desired on Oriental or Yak hair, a holding spray can be applied before crimping or waving, followed by a sheen spray. If any other formation is desired, the hair can be set with the appropriate rods or rollers, then dried under a hood dryer.

Indian or European hair is ordinarily not used in braided down braid styles. If either is used, you can spray on some hot water—followed by a holding gel—and let the braids dry naturally or use a dryer. Note that these types of hair should be kept oil-free to avoid a skimpy look. If Indian or European hair is braided with the ends left loose, it can be dried, then curled, crimped or waved like Oriental or Yak hair. If Indian or European hair has a permanent curl process formation, hair can be resprayed with water, brushed with a good plastic blow drying brush, and curls will reappear. If more curl or luster is needed, use glaze or sculpting lotion. If any other formation is desired, set hair with the appropriate rods or rollers, then dry. Note that these instructions for the care and maintenance of the more intricate, time-consuming braid extension styles are for all human hair braid extension work—whether the braids are braided all the way down or left loose at the ends. These instructions, however, do not apply to the care and maintenance of synthetic hair.

For the care and maintenance of intricate or time-consuming braid work with synthetic hair, the hair should be braided down. If braid styles are loose at the ends, braid down before proceeding with the following instructions. (Additional aid—rubber band, etc., can be used if needed to make sure the braid ends stay closed). 1) Use a hair and skin antiseptic to preclean your client's scalp. 2) Warm oil can be applied to the client's scalp between braids. 3) Rub scalp gently while using an infrared lamp; put a plastic cap on your client's head and keep client under the infrared lamp for about ten minutes for further penetration of hot oil treatment. 4) Let your client's head cool and then wash with a good cleansing shampoo using lukewarm water. 5) Use additional conditioner if needed for more luster. 6) Dry client's hair under a hood dryer using moderate heat. 7) Unbraid client's hair. If setting is required to maintain the previous formation of the original braid style, apply setting or holding gel to the damp braid before setting. 8) Finally, dry under a hood dryer using moderate heat.

Client's Responsibility for the Care and Maintenance of Their Braid Extensions

You can advise your clients who need touch-ups one to two weeks after the initial braiding that they can keep their braid styles looking continuously neat and have a clean, fresh scalp by using a hair and skin astringent every three to seven days, as needed. For everyday care, hot water can be sprayed on daily after positioning hair in a proper form for style and tying it with a scarf for a few minutes before starting the day. For your clients who need a touch-up after three to four weeks, the following procedures should be followed whether human or synthetic hair was used. Clients can apply hair and skin antiseptic to cotton or gauze and clean their scalps one to two weeks after the initial braid work, and again one to two weeks after a braid touch-up. The antiseptic not only cleans their hair, but helps to alleviate any itchiness. After applying hair and skin antiseptic, clients can rinse their hair under the shower if they wish, and dry with a towel.

If additional hair is Oriental or Yak and is braided all the way to the ends, your clients can apply petroleum jelly on shaft of hair down to the ends of braid, use holding spray, position braid style in its proper form, respray with warm water, then tie head with a scarf for a few minutes. For Oriental or Yak hair with braids left loose at the ends, your clients can thermocurl, crimp or wave hair electrically, or set with appropriate rods or curlers to achieve the initial formation. If the Oriental hair has been processed for permanent curl formation, a curl activator can be used. If Indian or European hair is used, and it is braided all the way down to the ends, hair can be resprayed with water after rinsing, and then a holding gel can be applied. Place additional holding gel on the braid from the shaft to the ends. Dry naturally or with a dryer. If braid style has been done with Indian or European hair and the braids are left loose, clients can dry hair and thermocurl it, wave or crimp electrically. For hair processed to have a permanent curl formation, glaze or processing lotion can be used. If synthetic hair has been used, client can apply, then rinse out the skin or hair antiseptic with warm to tepid water. Apply setting lotion or setting agent while hair is still damp; then set with rods, rollers, etc. and dry under a cool dryer or let hair dry naturally. (**Note:** Clients using synthetic hair should also be warned to protect their braid extension style with a cap when swimming to avoid matting of the synthetic hair).

A special note to students and cosmetologists—all clients wearing intricate or time-consuming braid extensions to the full life span, around two months, should be told that removing braid extensions is their responsibility. Due to the time needed to remove braid extensions, you can have a staff member remove braid extensions for a flat fee or an hourly charge. Your clients should also be given the following procedures for the proper removal and preparation before a rebraiding: 1) Wash and condition their hair a day or two before appointment. 2) After their braids dry, they should carefully remove all their braid extensions (a tail comb might be quite helpful at this point). Client should keep all clean additional hair in an orderly fashion. All short lengths and all longer lengths should be kept separate. A string or cord should be tied around braids to keep them in order. Your clients should not brush or comb additional hair removed to prevent misuse and waste. They should give you the additional hair so they can hackle hair to straighten it out if needed. Hackling will separate the hair and put it back in the condition it was in when purchased.

Conclusion

To recap, you should realize the importance of the proper care and maintenance of your clients' braid extensions. You should also stress to your clients the need to take some responsibility in the upkeep of their braid extension styles to ensure a continuous neat appearance and a clean, healthy scalp. Assure your clients that they have chosen a type of hair addition that will lead to strong, healthy new hair growth. Also, let them know they can call about their braid extensions if they have any questions.

CHAPTER

10 HOW TO INTRODUCE AND PROMOTE BRAID EXTENSION IN YOUR BEAUTY SALON

Braid extensions serve a dual purpose—to enhance beauty and to remedy damaged hair. Braid extensions aren't just a passing fad—they're here to stay. As a salon owner or manager, you must include braid extension work with your other services if you want to have a full-service establishment.

Unlike other types of hair additions, braid extensions let your client's hair rest from relaxers, excessive combing, brushing or pulling, since all the client's hair is intertwined in the braid—whether the extensions are visible or invisible, simple or intricate.

Other hair addition techniques include weaving (machine weaving, sewing method weaving, on scalp space braided track weave), integration, interlocking, bonding (which needs an adhesive), or fusing. Fusing is done with a heat conducting tool and generally leaves out 1/4 to 1/2 of the client's own hair to blend with the additional hair to achieve a more natural look. If your client's hair is chemically abused, the hair left out can suffer further damage such as too much combing, brushing or pulling. Although some salons use other weaving methods—like the on scalp braid track method where most of client's hair is inserted into tracks, and the interlock method which allows most of the client's own hair to rest from abuse—both of these methods insert most of the client's hair into horizontal or vertical braid tracks that make hair weave bulky. The tracks are easily felt when touched, especially if the client has a lot of hair to be inserted into the track. When using these methods, hairdressers sometimes leave out 1/16 to 1/8 of the client's own hair in the front, back and sides to comb over the weave for a more natural look.

Most clients do not want anyone to detect or ask them about horizontal or vertical tracks in their hair. They prefer hair weave additions like hair integration, fusing or bonding, where there is not much track at the scalp to show they are wearing hair additions. Clients would much rather have their friends or mates touch and admire their braid extensions than notice a weave track. If the interlocking weave method is used and on very thick hair, horizontal and vertical tracks will meet at the base of the scalp.

Difficulty arises in not being able to thoroughly cleanse the client's scalp and hair when shampooing, since most of client's hair is inserted into these horizontal and vertical braided tracks that meet each other. Braid extensions give your clients the convenience of being able to wear simple styles like the simple French braid or the large cornrow braid without detection of additional hair. These styles are popular, but the wearer usually must have long hair. However, with extensions, clients with short hair can enjoy these styles and have a totally natural look in which the sides of the hair can be combed flat to the scalp. If the French braid or large cornrow braid was attempted using a different weave method, the braider would have to take extreme precaution that the track would not be exposed.

Some clients with certain hair problems will eventually try to totally rest their own hair from further damage and will want braid extensions. Or, a client might simply want to experience having braid extensions for the beauty they create by adding length, body, intricate artwork or exaggerated height to the hair. Whether your clients choose the simple French braid or large cornrow braid, whether their braid extensions are visible or not, wearing braids is a positive experience. Clients will be seeking beauty shops that offer braid extension services, so it's important for you to keep up with current beauty trends so you can meet your clients' needs. By adding braid extensions to your salon, you will gain a reputation for proficiency and a boost in profits.

Before you introduce braid extensions to your salon, you should take a course in braid extensions. The course will benefit you whether you do the actual braiding in your salon or hire a braider. It will make you aware of the art of braid extension; and if you do hire a braider, you will know exactly what the braider is doing and what is and is not acceptable. Also, you will be able to perform the services of the braider to prevent a cancellation. If a client has a complaint about a braider's work, you will be also be able to rectify any problems.

How to Screen and Hire a Braider

The first step in hiring a braider for applying braid extensions is to contact a few top local beauty schools who teach braid extension application, and request one or two of their top braiders who will soon be graduating or have already graduated. These potential braiders should have a reputation of excellence in this field. You can also place ads in your local or national newspapers. Running ads might attract some braiders who have already graduated from a beauty school, or an experienced braider looking for a job. These potential braiders usually demand a higher commission, or whatever salary arrangement is agreed on. Whether you get a braider from a beauty school or in response to a newspaper ad, you must screen them as follows:

1) Check finger dexterity and control over braid work (as mentioned in Chapter 6, 6-10).

2) Check preciseness of parting of client's hair (no sloppy parting).

3) Watch the way the braider handles additional hair to avoid waste (excessive waste would be quite expensive if you are supplying the additional hair to be used).

4) Have the braider apply several small individual braids using small partings on client's hair and little additional hair. The braider should complete the braids all the way to the end of braid. Check the braider's ability to use discretion in picking up roughly the same amount of hair for each braid. Next, check to see how uniform individual braids are. Remember, applying additional hair should be undetectable, and parting when doing individual braids should be in brick-like formation (review Chapter 6, 6-1).

5) Next, have the braider apply several cornrow braid extensions. Remember, precise partings are very important here. After the braider has braided several cornrow braid extensions next to each other, check the closeness of the cornrows, making sure there is not too much parting and space showing. You will have a chance to see how well braiders use their discretion in deciding if extra additional hair needs to be fed in during the braiding to eliminate excessive spacing (as discussed in Chapter 6, 6-6).

6) Obviously, it isn't possible to test a potential braider on the outcome of a braid style that might take several hours. However, the five steps discussed above can give you an idea of the braider's capabilities. You can request that braiders do a simple, complete braid extension style like one of the simple styles explained and illustrated in Chapter 6, 6-11. Here, a simple large cornrow braid extension or a French braid with additional hair is applied at the back of the client's hair. The braider can then style the front of the client's hair in any way he or she chooses. You will get an idea of the braider's ability to perfect a completed style to suit the client's liking, and can see the braider's true ability of mastering the art of feeding in hair—a process that's the key to successfully completing these simple yet popular styles.

It is also important to see how well the braider can handle different situations—whether the client's hair is straight, curly, tightly curled, short and thick, short and thin or chemically damaged.

When you're screening a potential braider, you should make sure the braider demonstrates the following:

1) Good finger dexterity and control over braid work.

2) Uses precise parting on client's hair.

3) Handles additional hair to avoid waste.

4) Demonstrates application of individual extensions—
   a. Applies braids uniformly
   b. Applies additional hair that is undetectable
   c. Applies braids in brick-like formation

5) Shows application of cornrow braid extensions—
   a. Applies cornrows with little or no spaces or visible parting
   b. Shows the art of feeding in hair

6) Demonstrates a simple style that requires feeding in hair

Promoting Braid Extensions in Salons

Having screened your potential braiders, you can then choose the one who performed best and will be best suited for your salon needs. The braider you select should be given plenty of time before starting to work on a regular basis. This time, however, should be used productively to promote braid extension work in your salon, and the braider should play an active role in promotional efforts.

The first step to promoting braids in salons is to inform customers that you will be adding braid extensions to other services in your salon and that you will have braiders who are highly skilled in this area. Let your customers know your salon will be conducting a braid extension clinic.

Explain that clients' questions will be answered at this clinic, and that they can actually scrutinize and touch models' hair that has been braided already, or—if they wish—watch a simple braid extension style being applied from beginning to end.

The second step is to get a list of all volunteer models, a list of everyone attending the clinic, and a reminder to clients that refreshments will be served after the clinic. Volunteer models will not only wear a free braid extension style, they will also be excellent advertisements for your salon. Contact the braider to participate in the promotional clinic, and pay them a set fee for their services.

The third step is to involve the braider beforehand by having them braid a couple of intricate styles and a few styles requiring several hours. A braider may choose simple styles such as the ones shown in Chapter 6, 6-11 to demonstrate at the clinic.

The fourth step is the actual braid extension clinic, where your clients can actively participate in the clinic's setting, have all their questions on braid extensions answered, and find out how braid extensions can be used to enhance or change their present hair styles. Your clients can look at before-and-after pictures from this text to get a good idea of what can be done with braid extensions. They can volunteer to get a simple braid extension style done. They can also get a rough cost quote of the simplest to most intricate braid styles. While clients enjoy their refreshments, you could use this time to take appointments for braid extension work.

After you have successfully introduced braid extension services to your immediate clientele, you can then use the following steps to introduce braid extension to the public.

Introducing and Promoting Braid Extension to the Public

You can begin introducing braid extension services to the public by first going to speak to your hair suppliers. During this visit you should explain that your salon will be providing expert braid extension services, and can show suppliers pictures of hair styles done by braiders during the clinic. If you had purchased hair from that hair supplier for your clinic, you can assure the supplier of your intention to buy a considerable amount of hair from them in the future.

You can then ask hair suppliers to post some of their pictures showing "befores" and "afters" taken during the clinic, and request that they hang fliers next to pictures in their stores. You should also leave a few business cards with suppliers. Note that you must use your discretion when posting or displaying your braid extension work with hair suppliers or beauty suppliers. For example, you should use pictures showing the type of hair the supplier sells. If a supplier usually sells Oriental hair, then try to display more pictures with Oriental hair instead of other types. It's best, however, to leave more pictures and fliers with suppliers that deal with a wider variety of hair. These suppliers will be better able to accommodate clients with different hair types. When advertising your braid extension services at stores that sell mainly synthetic hair, display photographs showing braid styles with synthetic hair. Showing the pictures with the type of hair the merchant sells serves as a dual advertisement: you get more clients, and the merchant gets more sales. This advantage can be pointed out during the discussion with merchants—whether they're hair suppliers, beauty suppliers, owners or managers of wig shops, discount shops, drug stores or any store that sells hair products or cosmetics.

The techniques of advertising braid extension services discussed in this chapter are the keys to successfully introducing braid extension services in salons. To review: 1) By conducting a braid extension clinic, salon owners or managers can introduce braid extensions to clients, clients' friends as well as clients' families. 2) By building a rapport with hair suppliers, beauty suppliers, owners or managers of wig shops, discount stores, some drug stores, or any store that sells hair products and cosmetics or supplies hair, you can advertise with the help of these merchants—gaining new customers while the merchant sees increased sales. 3) You should try to be acquainted with beauty suppliers who sell different types of human hair, and explain to these merchants that by advertising your braid extension services, they will also benefit because of increased sales of their products.

After successfully advertising and following through to ensure client satisfaction, you will see that the greatest advertisement in the beauty business is word of mouth from highly pleased clients. However, you should **continue** to advertise in local newspapers and distribute fliers locally to further build your new braid extension clientele.

To salon owners or managers, students and cosmetologists, good luck in your endeavor. Your success will mean more recognition for salons, increased profits and a wonderful sense of accomplishment.

BIBLIOGRAPHY

1. Cooper, Wendy. *Hair, Sex, Society, Symbolism.* New York: Stein and Day Publishers, 1971.

2. Corson, Richard. *Fashions in Hair: The First Thousand Years.* London: Peter Owen, 1965.

3. DeNegri, Eve. *Nigerian Body Adornment.* Lagos: Academy Press, 1976.

4. Farr, Francine. "Cornrows and Individuals: Afro-American Braid Styles in Los Angeles." *Ornament,* June 1983, Vol. VI, No. 4, pp. 12–15.

5. Gwatkin, Nina W. *Yoruba Hairstyles.* Lagos, Nigeria: The Craft Center National Museum Compound, 1971.

6. Jones, John Henry, and Lois L. Jones. *All About the Natural.* USA. Clairol Incorporated, 1971.

7. Lagarus, Elizabeth. "Ease of Care, Cultural Identity Woven into Hair Styles." *The Washington Post,* 15 Jan. 1988.

8. Ogunwale, Titus. *African Traditional Hairdos.* International Women's Year — 1975.

9. Rosen, Norma. "Wearable Coils: Nigerian Hair Sculpture." *Common Threads,* July/August 1985, pp. 33–35.

10. Rosenbaum, Helen. *The Braid Book.* New York: Wallaby Books, 1979.

11. Thomas, Valerie. Accent Africa: *Traditional and Contemporary Hairstyles for the Black Woman.* New York: Col-Bob Associates, 1973.

GLOSSARY

1. *Additional Hair*—The initial hair added to client's hair to form an extended braid.

2. *Braid Extension*—Applying additional hair braided into clients' hair to give additional length and body, and to rest their hair from chemical and other types of abuse.

3. *Brick-Like Formation Partings*—Checkerboard pattern partings used in individual and invisible braid extensions to conceal partings of the previous rows of braids.

4. *Cornrow Braid Extension*—A technique in which small portions of client's hair are picked up from scalp with the additional hair to form a continuous underhand braid.

5. *Detectable Braid Extension*—A braid extension applied with a loop exposed at the base of client's braid, indicating additional hair has been added.

6. *Extra Additional Hair*—The extra hair added if needed after the "Additional Hair" has been added to obtain a more proportional individual braid extension that is braided down to the end, and to acquire wider widths in cornrow braid extension.

7. *Feeding-In-Hair*—The gradual application of the extra additional—to be added as often as needed without any detection.

8. *Individual Braid Extensions (box braids)*—Applying additional hair to small box-like portions of clients' hair to create a braid extension.

9. *Intricate Braid Extensions*—Time-consuming braid extension styles (many intricate styles are braided in up-braid styles where braids are enjoyed for their artwork).

10. *Invisible Braid Extensions*—Individual braid extensions in which the braids are not braided down to the ends (ends left loose).

11. *Overhand Braiding*—When right and left portions of hair overlap the center portion of hair alternately, and when palms of hand are facing downward during the overlapping process.

12. *Partial Cornrow and Individual Braid Extensions*—Combination of cornrow and individual braid extensions.

13. *Precision Partings*—Defined partings that are free from any unwanted hair.

14. *Proportional Braids*—Braids that are relatively the same size from beginning to end.

15. *Simple Braid Extension Styles*—Braid extension styles that require little time to create. For example, one cornrow or French braid at back of client's head.

16. *Underhand Braiding*—When right and left portions of hair are placed under center portion of hair alternately to become the new center, and when palms of hands are facing up during braiding process.

17. *Undetectable Braid Extension*—Braid extensions applied without any detection that additional hair has been added. No exposed loop at base of braid.

18. *Visible Braid Extensions*—When all braid work can be seen. For example, individual braids braided down to the end and cornrow braid extensions.

ADDING LENGTH WITH BRAID EXTENSIONS

BRAID EXTENSIONS WITH ORIENTAL HAIR

Before.

After, with loose French braid extension — front view.

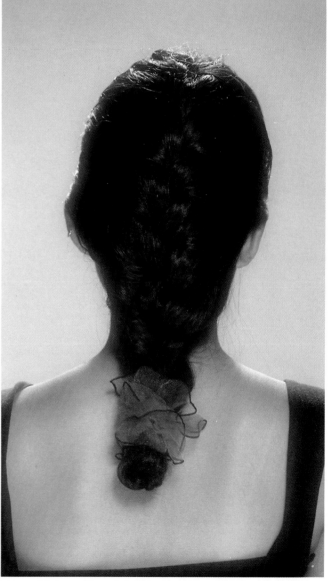

After, with loose French braid extension — back view.

A NEW LOOK WITH BRAID EXTENSIONS

Before.

After.

Before.

After, with invisible braid extension.

Upbraid hairstyle — back view.

Upbraid hairstyle — front view.

HANDSOME HAIR!

REDHEADS HAVE MORE FUN!

BRAIDS IN ALL LENGTHS!